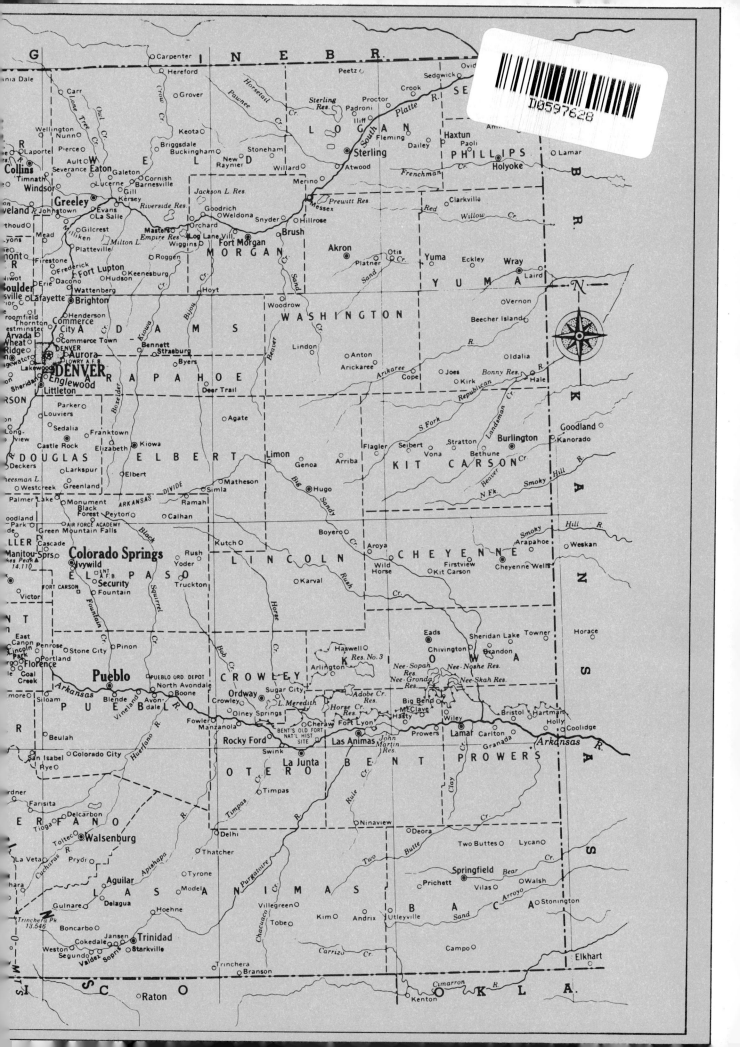
I0597628

COLORADO
Big Mountain Country

Mount Sneffels, 14,150 feet high, pinnacle of the San Juan Mountains, 42 miles south of Montrose.

COLORADO
Big Mountain Country

REVISED EDITION

PHOTOGRAPHY BY MYRON WOOD
STORY BY NANCY WOOD

DOUBLEDAY & COMPANY, INC., GARDEN CITY, NEW YORK

Library of Congress Catalog Card Number 69–12192
Copyright © 1969, 1972 by Myron Wood and Nancy Wood
All Rights Reserved
Printed in the United States of America
First Edition

To Marie Rodell

Contents

Acknowledgments

ALTHOUGH ONLY TWO NAMES appear as authors of this book, many others are involved without whose help *Colorado: Big Mountain Country* would still be only an idea. We owe special thanks to: Helen Bonfils whose grant in 1963 enabled approximately one-half of the photographs to be shot during the next several years and 30,000 miles; to Robert O'Connor of Doubleday who thought there ought to be a Colorado book; to Ray Simpson of Doubleday who knew there was a market; to T. O'Conor Sloane III, our editor, who understood our necessities; to James Perry and the First National Bank of Colorado Springs who put faith behind its money; to Marie Rodell, our friend and agent, for patience, suggestions, constant support, and initial layout ideas; and to Herman Raymond and Bishop Nash for assistance in technical problems and design; to the National Park Service and the Soil Conservation Service for special help and considerations. Nancy Wood especially wishes to thank Bob Hilkey, Ferry Carpenter, and Tom Lasater for teaching her to see and understand Colorado and Roy Stryker who at the beginning of the project said, "You have to remain objective while being subjective on both sides," and this is what she tried to do.

Thanks also go to Joy Schendel, who typed the manuscript; Marshall Sprague, who was the final authority on history, and Norman Sams, librarian, who helped with the index.

Our deepest gratitude goes to Michael Gamer who gave countless hours to the preparation of work prints and reproduction prints and assisted greatly in the final tedious layout. And finally we thank our four children—Karen, Chris, Kate and India—for being patient for one whole year.

NANCY AND MYRON WOOD
Colorado Springs, Colorado
March 1969

The gap between then and now is shorter here.

Introduction

THEY WORE COWBOY BOOTS creased to the shape of their feet and the angle of their stirrups. Their belts were hand-tooled leather. The silver buckles were designed with a monogram or with the name of a county rodeo won with the skill they had spent their lives acquiring. Not one ate with his hat off.

Behind the counter, a large middle-aged woman in a white uniform stood over the grill, frying a couple of frozen T-bones. She wiped her hands on her apron and came over to the men.

"My poor little dog," she said, and she took from her pocket a small plastic jar filled with gallstones. She rolled them on the table, like dice or the way they do in that part of the state with the first picking of piñon nuts.

I watched and wondered how long it would be before no one did that anymore. How long before the naturalness wore off or got buried, in the name of progress. How long before what brought us to Colorado and has held us here all these years is gone.

The uneasiness comes when the seasons change or when the surveyors' strings start fluttering in a forest I thought was safe. Then I ask myself whether it will really matter when a dog's gallstones aren't rolled out on a café table anymore? Will it really matter when some other important things are gone or become so mixed up and changed that no one gives a damn?

For who has heard of Wild Horse and Yoder? Who has seen a pair of golden eagles soaring above a back road of Fort Carson on a Sunday afternoon when the guns are still and no one is out tearing up the land that used to be good? Who has felt the wind rushing up a canyon at Mesa Verde, blowing over an unnamed ruin? Who cares that antelope run in the San Luis Valley at sunset when the Sangre de Cristos glow in immense and choking splendor?

The world is hard up for simple things.

What will take the place of a little girl selling "lemonade, roses, rocks, and nosegays"? What will replace the toothless, split-nailed ranch woman dressed like an unmade bed, whose goats, sheep, horses, dogs, and guinea hens gossip in the dust of a barnyard? What will happen to the small prairie town with no church and no movie house and no drugstore, where the United Nations bar is the only one in town and the one flag flying has forty-eight stars? What will become of Edward Eyetooth in the Mancos Canyon, who sleeps under a cottonwood arbor in summer?

The writing of this book arose from a search for human values—the meaning of the land by itself, the meaning of the people fused to the land. We learned not to care much for camper trucks, new jeeps, motorbikes, drunken hunters, so-called "land management," ski resorts, surface mining, the Bureau of Public Roads and the Bureau of Reclamation. It was the myth that we searched for, the myth being taken away by all these manifestations of progress.

Once in a while we found that myth or a remnant of it. And that is what we photographed and wrote about. But we also photographed and wrote about reality and asked ourselves, where does one end and the other begin? One cannot always tell, especially here, where space blurs time, reason, and credibility.

This is a lot of land to tame. When I stand at timberline and look out across the vastness I cannot believe it will be tamed. Yet, in one century or two at most, it will be.

And so I say, like many another lover of this land: I want no monument, no flowers, no marker, and no memorial. Just save the last mountain for me.

NANCY WOOD
Colorado Springs, Colorado
March 1969

COLORADO
Big Mountain Country

Plains

FROM JULESBURG TO STONINGTON, between Sand Arroyo and the North Fork of the Cimarron River, over to the Purgatoire and the Apishapa and north again to the towns of Delhi, Cheraw, Deertrail, and Last Chance, the land is the color of the color relief map. The tawny brown spreads over forty thousand square miles, broken here and there by a sprinkling of cottonwoods along the rivers and by the fields of the dry land farmers. There is as much as seventy-five miles between the places with the funny names, places inconspicuous save for their conspicuous names.

On a lonely road connecting three communities so small that the post office is merely a cage inside a gas station sits a row of mailboxes. The mailboxes are clustered together and the intense sun bounces off them and illuminates the black letters of their names. There is not a house in any direction, not a sign of human habitation except a field of crested wheat, pale gold and stretching away to the green of a creek bottom. The wheat belongs to one of them, a name unknown except around those little communities. But the name goes back to when the land was unbroken and represents its entire civilized history.

Out there, where the trees vanish and the land sets off in a dry land roll of grassy ocean, where the muted colors rise like mist, and the sky bears down on the horizon, out there on an unbelievable space where even sound

Before a roundup near Hanover, southeast of Colorado Springs.

Spring on the plains near Calhan. (Overleaf)

[5]

Deserted farm west of Boyero near Cheyenne Wells.

seems hushed lives a breed of men and women who are an extension of that land. The ones who are dedicated have been there a long time and will be there until they die. They came, some of them, when the century turned, and fused themselves to the earth, making the best of the sorry land that was given them for nothing.

There are not many still alive who go that far back themselves, but the second and third generations are still around, trying to hang onto the land, increased a hundredfold by now and worth perhaps a cool million. Even that which a realtor calls "all snake infested and crap-earthed," the unimproved and dead-dry land, commands as much as fifty dollars an acre. Those who cannot resist the offers are selling out and some gravitate toward the big cities and for the first time in their lives find they have nothing to do. They have the money all right, and a few are tempted to blow it, but these are people who never in their lives have missed rising with the sun and going to bed with it, with an uncommon amount of labor in between. To those who have not sold out, either for reasons of waiting for higher prices or simply because they cannot bear to give up a lifetime's work, the ones with

Harold Hoover, pioneer homesteader, Rush.

full pockets are neither condemned nor condoned. Out there in prairie country each man's choice is his own.

"Yessir, I was the first ever to put a plow to it. A couple million years old it is and virgin till ought-five," said an eighty-five-year-old homesteader who has resisted all government help, including the Soil Conservation Service. His lanky body filled the chair in a set of right angles, like a dying cornstalk. He was uncomfortable in the house and he looked out the open door to his fields.

"A man don't amount to much if he hasn't done it hisself," he said, and told how he still worked fifteen hours a day, drove a tractor, and tended several hundred head of cattle alone. "I don't know where it all went . . . or when," he said of time in a voice that seemed to come out of the prairie wind. "I got a nice little garden over the hill. It's not very big but it's as clean as you'll find anywhere." The garden was something he could feel, the same way he felt his numbered days. "If I have to go into town I get the fidgets." His time was precious, his days few, his friendships lean. To the city visitor he remarked, "You are obliged to like people. I am obliged to like no one."

Cowboys saddling up at dawn during a drought year.

His wife, also in her eighties, was partially blind. She, too, was a homesteader when barely out of her teens, and came out with a couple of cousins
who weren't old enough to vote but claimed their 160 acres anyway. "We
had a ball," she recalled, the old eyes distant and proud and filmed over. Had
it ever got lonely? "Why, no," she said, astonished, "why should it?"

At dusk the old rancher went out to his barn, excusing himself. "I have
to comply with routine. When the chickens need taking care of, I do it.
Them and the cattle." He wondered what would happen when he was gone.
It would not be long. His ears, frostbitten when he was young, developed
cancer a few years before and were removed. He had been to all the special-

ists, taken all the treatments. "Now I treat it myself with spirits of gum turpentine. Same as I use on the calves and the ewes."

Southwest of there is another homesteader, a vibrant, toothless man in his late sixties. "I fool with those chickens," he said, backing out of the hen house. He also raises wheat. "When that old southwest wind is a-blowin' high and the wheat is wavin' and them cattle are on the buffalo grass, it ain't Detroit or Los Angeles I'm seein'." His eyes became excited as he looked across the fields that had felt his sweat for fifty years. "Guess you wonder why we homesteaded here. Well, it was poor folks like us who settled here. Rich ones looked at it and walked away. We lived on potatoes and jack rabbits a long time. Then we planted a little corn and a little beans, a few beets, got on to some cattle. It waren't so bad. Leastways we didn't starve and there was a lot of sky to look at and land to ride along when we wasn't plowin' it."

Farther out on the prairie, near where the Purgatoire flows into the Arkansas are what people call the "Flint Hills." Actually, they are made of sandstone and the rutted, meandering roads to the isolated ranches are covered with broken fragments of it, as if put there by a thoughtful but derelict road crew. It has been a wet year but the buffalo grass is tawny, not green. The white faces, requiring forty acres each, gnaw on it thoughtfully, scarcely looking up as they chew their way along. The land here is as barren as any on the prairie, yet there is a gentle beauty to it. The ground swells and breaks into ridges, then rises and plunges off abruptly into dry washes and gullies. There are no trees except the cottonwoods, willows, and box elders which grow in and along the creek bottoms. Cactus and yucca cling to the soil; in the bare spots the earth has been "clodded up" to prevent its blowing away.

In summer, no matter how much rainfall, the sun sears the land with murderous intensity. The wind cuts with a dusty edge and the rain, when it comes, seems to have been hurled from the sky. In winter, suffocating blizzards cover the cattle and obliterate landmarks, leaving the prairie like a dead sky, toneless, empty, and silent. It is the kind of place that seems to have no end and man is made giddy by the fact that, though the ground passes under his feet, he seems to be in exactly the same place he started from. Time has been held back so far but it is beginning to spill across the prairie, gathering up all the little farms and ranches whose only fault was that they stood still.

Encompassing some of the Flint Hills and some of the Purgatoire is a 33,000 acre ranch run by a bachelor. His father was a Basque sheepherder who homesteaded in the 1890s and took his wages in sheep. He parlayed this into herds totaling 30,000 head and became prosperous. The son, who

Livestock barn, Colorado State Fair at Pueblo.

Old Spanish-American gravemarker.

remembers living in a tent when he was small, also went into the sheep business but sold out in 1951 because of a drought and a shortage of help. A rich man by any standards, this rancher, now in his fifties, has no intention of getting out. His life's work will go, and is already going, to nieces, nephews, and friends, all of whom, ever since they were born, have received gifts of calves. His house, fairly new, is large and comfortable and furnished with a color television and modern furniture. Three bedrooms are for his relatives who drive out frequently and spend the night; he himself sleeps in the base-

Architectural detail, Pueblo.

ment. An auto accident a number of years ago broke his back and has kept him off horses ever since. He walks with difficulty but takes it with the Spanish attitude that "all life is pain and I'll make the best of it."

Stubborn, hardworking, and honest, this rancher, like the other two, has had his share of heartbreak and failure. Nothing diminishes them and nothing can make them accept the fact that because of a lucky accident of rising land values, they are now wealthier than most men in the state. To them, success is not measured by what the land gives in terms of real-estate dollars but by what it has been made to yield, against its will, in terms of cattle and crops. The land value is a cushion if all else should fail and they will not submit to it without losing their own integrity. They are disturbed by the mention of what the land is worth and speak instead of their own intangibles: the freedom to do as they please, the business of caring for the creatures, the feeling they get by being part of a basic system that has sustained man for eons.

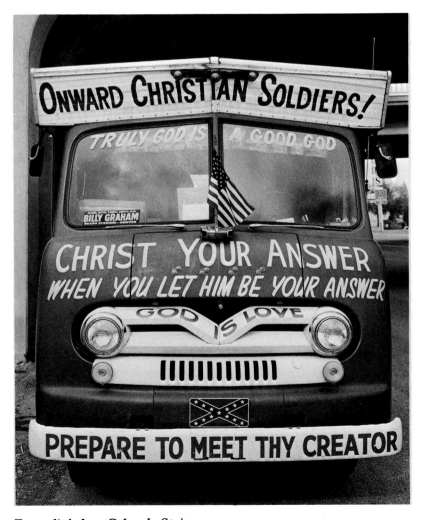

Evangelist's bus, Colorado Springs.

It was a hundred and one in Lamar. Locusts crackled in the elm trees in front of the plain little houses in the old part of town. Here, as in other towns along the prairie, life is lived with little intensity. Even the traffic seems slower except that which zooms along the interstates in four lanes of fury. If life is a little slower, if the breath of the towns is playing out and their pulse consigned to a steady, slow beat of old age, there is also something remarkably touching in the way these old prairie places retain a certain inner radiance. True, they have all the ailments of small towns—gossip, jealousy, stagnation—but there are other things as well: a sense of humor, an openness, an ability to make small jokes about themselves, a cheery goodnaturedness, a love for spontaneous conversation with strangers on sidewalks, in stores, and in the middle of the street. Their ties with one another are strong, sometimes going back as many years as the town itself. Old-timers still talk about coming out in wagons, following the old trails and claiming the land and starting out with perhaps a blacksmith shop or a general store or a hundred head of cattle.

If you ask any one of them why they live there they will tell you they have always lived there and they like it. They like the closeness of one another, the feeling of being safely tucked away from the dangers of the world, and for those over fifty, they like their town because it is the same as it always was. They sit on their porches, face turned to the air and sunshine; they water a little patch of vegetables or petunias in a billowy row along the house; they gaze at pictures of a healthy lot of children, grown and gone, with their likenesses in frames on top of the television set; they walk into town to mail a letter and sit on benches under the trees, talking, remembering, lapsing into silence as the wind stirs the cottonwoods and the smell of alfalfa drifts across the open fields.

Micheletti building, La Veta.

Railroad yard, Lamar.

From the Kansas line westward the prairie towns are mostly laid out along the rivers and the railroads, sometimes both. From a distance they sit on a horizon whose color and clouds appear to have come from a paint-by-number kit. Near Kansas are the grain elevator towns, their fat shafts sticking way up in the sunlight and dwarfing the little structures below. Intermingled with the grain towns are the sugar towns, some with refineries from which comes the autumn stink of processed pulp.

In a landscape starved for detail, it is here in the towns, with neat yards and clean, shaded streets, that detail flourishes. But the towns resemble one another and it is hard, later, to sort them out and attach special significance to any one in particular. Unpretentious, isolated, and ordinary, the towns are the centers for the vast farms and ranches which surround them. They do not exist for tourists, and accommodations, though clean, are not numerous and often vintage. One small town hotel offers rooms for three dollars with the bathroom shared with five other rooms, usually occupied by genial salesmen of farm equipment. The food is simple, reasonably priced, and nearly universal throughout the plains. Potatoes are served with breakfast, chili is available anytime, and steaks are number one on the menu.

Here and there in a prairie town is a graceful old piece of architecture which may house an Elks Hall, a post office, Christians, or a long-gone livery. A simple little frame house may have nothing to distinguish it except a stained-glass window set high in a gable. The train stations, sleepy and in need of repair, wait mostly for freight shipments and even those are becoming less and less frequent. The mighty diesel trucks now link the plains communities, shaking the windows as they roar into a straightaway in the middle of the night.

These are towns of middle-aged people and their tastes are reflected in well-attended churches, frequent suppers for livestock associations, and fashions in the store windows which are, like their buyers, solid and dependable. Children from ranch and town usually attend consolidated schools, riding as much as seventy-five miles one way. The quality of their education has improved greatly since Ford Foundation money enabled school boards to invest in better teachers and methods in the late fifties. There are still a number of back-road schools, however, built early in the century, which refuse to consolidate. The playgrounds are forlorn, the classrooms poorly lighted, and there is nothing to keep the dirt from blowing through the open windows.

Sad, quiet, and proud, the prairie towns ask for no pity. The inhabitants like them the way they are and point to low rates of crime, accidents, suicides, divorces, and disease. The birth rate is down and some towns have neither doctor nor dentist. With automobiles and fast roads, centers like Limon, Sterling, Trinidad, Pueblo, Colorado Springs, and Denver are never more than a half-day's drive for anyone on the prairie.

[16]

Ranches at Matheson.

Living on the same prairie and loving it not any less are men who came out a decade or so ago, enamoured of the West. Backed by family money and an Ivy League education, these men bought up one, two, or three ranches. Immaculately groomed, discussing genetics or Greek history with equal ease, they appear at social events in Denver, vacation in Mexico, Hawaii, and Europe and send their children to select prep schools. Their cattle are usually registered Herefords, Angus, or Santa Gertrudis. They often experiment with crossbreeding, enter their bulls at competitions, and, if they want to make money, are changing their operation to steers, usually imported from Mexico. If they need money, the banks lend them all they can possibly need for the land value is rising faster than the interest. Like the homesteaders and their descendants, who sometimes have to go to the bank, too, the new cattleman loves his land and all the things he does for it and on it. Calving, roundups, branding, shipping—he is in the midst of it on horseback, working hard and feeling that rugged individualism creeping through his pores.

Prairie hawk hung on barbed-wire fence.

Abandoned church north of Simla.

A far-sighted cattleman has said that fifty years hence we will look back on this period of cattle raising as the most backward, poorly planned and poorly executed enterprise of all time, nonetheless there is something renewing and rewarding about working with cattle out in the open. Even though hauling them from winter to summer pasture is proved impractical, even though the entire cattle business could and should be streamlined, men enjoy being cowboys. There is a sport to it and it answers something very basic in their natures.

"You might as well tell a hunter that from now on he can pick up his deer at the corner Safeway than tell these cowboys they can't do all this cute stuff anymore," says one critic. As for the fun-loving cattlemen, they seem to feel: forget practicality. It will compromise us soon enough.

There is yet another type of individual who is associated with the prairie, one who is referred to with spit before the tag of "outsider" is fastened to him. The "outsider" is the one whom the homesteaders hate most and the one who is blamed or credited with bringing a whole new era to the prairie.

"The southerners are taking our churches and the Texans are taking our land," complained one old-time rancher. Texan, Kansan, Oklahoman, or from either coast, the man under the big Stetson wearing expensive boots and monogrammed shirts and probably flying his own airplane, is turning agriculture into corporate industry with all the accouterments of tax write-offs, showcasing, and depersonalization. The townspeople, the homesteader, the small rancher, all of these are being crowded out by smart businessmen, including the man with the most money, the "outsider." Often the "outsider" merely represents a huge corporation—aluminum, steel, oil—and turns over all ranch operations to a highly trained manager.

"But the fact of it is," said a man whose lifetime has been in cattle, "these damn big outfits are the only ones who can afford to ranch. Taxes, land prices, labor, you name it, it's against us. So the chairman of the board of some huge company says, 'fellows, what do you want to do? We can buy another oil well, we can buy half of South America, or we can get us a cattle ranch.' Every man, from the time he saw Tom Mix in the movies, has wanted to be a cowboy and that's what gets the vote. A hundred years from now this prairie is going to be just one IBM of a cattle factory."

At least one place on the Colorado prairie is already counting on computers to aid the beef-cattle business. At Greeley, the center of Colorado's huge cattle-feeding industry, Farr Farms uses a nuclear-powered computer to determine moisture content and density of cattle feed. A maximum of nine thousand head of cattle consumes forty pounds of feed per day each at Farr's lot, keeping a fleet of trucks busy ten hours a day picking up feed from a machine which looks like a cement mixer. Bill Farr, the fourth generation of his family to operate Farr Farms, is a high-powered graduate of an agricultural college who points out that in twenty-five years feed lots may also be out of business because the grain concentrates now fed to cattle will be

Sign on abandoned gas station, Cheyenne Wells.

Haswell, center of dry-farming area near Kansas border.

Trinidad.

needed for human consumption. Feeders will either have to provide some kind of forage material for their cattle or else send them back to natural grassland. Farr realizes the predicament of ranchers in both buying and selling cattle and feels that much of the present dilemma stems from the fact that most of them have not waked up. The price of retail beef will go even higher predicts Farr who has added to his lot ten thousand male Holstein dairy cattle, fed, raised, and marketed as beef cattle.

Trinidad, on old Santa Fe Trail at foot of Raton Pass. Fisher's Peak in background.

Tom Lasater.

But Farr is not the only voice telling ranchers to wake up. Colorado's most controversial cattleman is Tom Lasater, who has created an entirely new breed of cattle which live on a ranch at Matheson that is run completely opposite to any in the West. Moreover, his theory of how ranchers ought to save themselves has brought resentment and criticism from many of the men he is trying to help.

A transplanted Texan whose father owned a 400,000 acre empire at Falfurrias, Lasater came to the Colorado prairie in 1949 under his own steam for at that point he had inherited no property from his father. While still in Texas, Lasater singlehandedly produced a new breed of cattle, the only man in history to do so all by himself. He calls his breed the Beefmaster and it is the result of a three-way cross between the Brahman, Shorthorn, and Hereford. A fantastically hardy and meaty beast, the Beefmaster has been accepted in nearly every beef-cattle state and has won strong acceptance abroad, with a steady flow of foreign cattlemen pouring into the ranch. When Lasater first came to Colorado, however, cattlemen placed bets on how long it would take the tropical animals to die during the cruel winter when temperatures plunged to twenty below and snow covered the grassland. But the animals, who had never seen snow, simply nosed it away to get at the grass. Conventional cattlemen pooh-pooh this story with, "Horses, not cattle, are the only critters smart enough to paw away snow."

Lasater has never bred any of his animals for the show ring and doesn't plan to. Their long backs, legs, ears, and variation in coloring would disqualify them immediately. This maverick cattleman is only interested in what lies under the skin and considers all other characteristics meaningless. He refuses to coddle his herd and forces them to rustle for themselves in any kind of weather without help from himself or the two men who work for him. When one rancher heard what Lasater put his cattle through he observed, "Being a Beefmaster is like being on the moon with a Boy Scout kit."

Beefmaster calves.

If Lasater's cattle cause the purebred associations to ignore him and most of the plainsmen to refer to them as Mixmasters and mongrels, his ranching techniques cause even greater disturbance. "The way we do it isn't good enough for him," snorted one rancher who loves to ride and rope. Lasater permits no roping, nor does he use an electric prodder or drag his animals to the branding iron. "His roundups are a farce," said another man. Indeed, all Lasater does on a roundup is drive his truck into the middle of a pasture and honk the horn. The cattle come running and he checks them over and drives away. "I don't do these things to be different," says Lasater. "The cute stuff just isn't practical."

As if that weren't enough, Lasater has made it his business to publicize the one word that is anathema to cattlemen: unionize. A union, he feels, is the only way for the cattleman to escape his sagging economy, by bargaining together against the giant supermarket chains. When he first mentioned his idea to a group of Colorado ranchers at a public meeting, there was a stunned silence. Only two men agreed with him. The rest were outraged.

Lasater, known all his life as a scrapper, faces an uphill climb. Most ranchers steer clear of him. His friends talk to him about everything except cattle. Most of the surrounding communities keep a wary eye on him. No one wants trouble and Lasater has caused plenty of it. He constantly challenges government subsidy, rails against the rancher with his hand stuck out, and once confronted an agricultural official who pretended not to see how a well-drilling program was being misused with, "Either you're a lying sonofabitch or a stupid sonofabitch. Take your choice." To all these barrel-stirrings, he is quick to reply, "If you want to be a top dog, don't act like a cur."

The death of a small town in America does not count for much. Small towns succumb to dams, farms to factories, forests to subdivisions; wilderness depreciates into real estate, mountains are divided by interstates, and rivers are coveted by the water politicians. This is called progress and anyone who has heard the cry for more knows that what thus passes from the American scene for the sake of it will not be missed by many. And so it was with a Colorado coal mining community that died not long ago.

Sopris used to sit on a dry piece of ground above a muddy river called the Purgatoire. The Purgatoire has its beginning in the Culebra Range of the Sangre de Cristo Mountains in the southern part of Colorado not far from the New Mexico border. As it makes its way down from the mountains, the river passes through Stonewall and Segundo, Primero and Weston, Valdez and some crumbling adobe villages whose names have disappeared from the map. And all along the route that the river takes as it runs down toward Trinidad, there is the indelible imprint of the Spanish-Americans—except for Sopris, which always belonged to the Italians.

For a long time—eighty-five years, to be exact—the Italians lived there, in houses made of stucco or wood or stone, good houses that held up well as families of eight and ten and twelve children grew up in them. The Italians came from the old country in the last century and settled the town of Sopris and spent their lives in the coal mines with a pick and shovel, digging out the stuff for Colorado Fuel and Iron for as little as three dollars a day for sixteen tons, just the way the song goes.

In their cellars they made wine from grapes shipped in from California. In their back yards they planted flowers and vegetables and built ovens for their women to bake the *pane.* They played *bocci* and *morra* (a game where

Small herd of antelope near Kutch.

not fewer than four players flip their fingers and call numbers in Italian), drank wine in their houses and beer at the taverns, kept their sons out of the mines, pushed hard for their children's education, fought with no one except the mine owners, did not disturb the peace nor disobey the church. Family married into family and raised another generation, and that generation stayed on, and by and by you could hardly tell Sopris from some town in Italy, so complete was it with family and tradition and community ties. At one time two thousand people lived along the dusty, winding streets of the "district"— Sopris, Piedmont, St. Thomas, and Jerryville all lumped together. Then the mines shut down in 1940 and the population dropped to about five hundred and stayed that way for years until a curious thing happened.

The government decided that Sopris had to die.

It had to die because the cranky Purgatoire flooded the town of Trinidad in a bad way about once every five years. The people there said no new business would come to Trinidad because of the way the river flooded. And so there had to be a dam and the dam had to be not far from the Piedmont bridge where long ago the little boys stood on top and watered the trolley cars. The dam and the reservoir that will bury Sopris under a hundred feet of water by 1975 will cost fifty-five million dollars, a sum approved by Congress in 1955. The dam will be made of Sopris itself—all the back yards, streets, gardens, pathways, and fields where a kid could fly a homemade kite or a four-propeller boomerang. Something else will go into the dam too. Something intangible. Something that linked all the people together for so many years and through so much sickness and so much poverty and so much despair that all they really had was the faith that nothing could kill them as a people.

Sopris somehow believed itself immortal.

There was always talk of a dam, as long ago as 1922, when eighteen men were blown to bits in the mine. But Sopris, being nearly a hundred feet above the river, never felt the floods, never listened seriously to the government men who talked of a dam, and finally did not believe that their town had to give its life for the sake of a dam.

Then some tangible evidence occurred. "Big Ed" Johnson, then senator from Colorado, and Edgar Chenoweth, then congressman for the third congressional district, pushed through the legislation after years of trying. The government appraiser showed up, slapped a price on houses that never did have a price, and told the people to move. Some did, and they tried to buy elsewhere what they had in Sopris and found it cost more. Some did not move, and they leased back from the government the homes in which they had been born and tried to make the best of things. When the last class was graduated from the high school in 1965 and the building was demolished, the sight of it was too much, like pictures they had seen of what happened to the land of their forefathers during the war. So the painful exodus began, lasting until only a few families remained, the ones who stuck it out until the winter of 1971, when the bulldozers finally put an end to the place.

Italian coal miners are a memorable lot. They have seen the good and bad of life, smelled death firsthand in the mines, taken care of their young and their old, remained loyal to their friends, and mashed the grapes with their feet during the last part of September. They did not belong to the Mafia. They were not ashamed to work with their hands. They did not complain about anything except conditions in the mines, and after a strike or two they began to be treated like human beings. Their faces stayed young, their bodies supple, their minds keen, their humors undiminished. They retired, sat on their porches, tended their gardens, drank their wine, and played with their grandchildren, who often lived as close as the house next door. They asked for nothing except to live out their days in Sopris.

But life did not work out that way, and it is said that some died on purpose rather than pack up and leave. When they did leave, they left behind certain things. A basket of wash in the yard. A crucifix on the coal stove. The last year's Christmas cards. A baseball glove. The perennial plants. The automobile, which did not run. The baby's shoes. The washing machine, which never got fixed. A drawer full of unpaid bills. A stack of grave-removal permits, for even the dead of Sopris had to be moved to higher ground. The discarded empty barrels in which wine had turned to vinegar and which could not be used again. Then those who had paid good money to do so came and removed the bathtubs, the staircases, the paneling, the plate-glass windows, and the front porches but left the rockers. Picked clean, the houses went down with one good whack from the bulldozer.

Sopris was not so immortal after all.

On the Fourth of July 1970, when Sopris was just about half dead and only a few families remained, there was a requiem for the town. It was neither sad nor sentimental but honest and simple and straight—the way the place had been. Some six hundred people came from far and wide to salute the town and not to mourn it, for the end had been a long time coming and they were resigned.

The old men stood arm in arm under the cottonwoods and the elms, glancing up at a jet streaking across a brittle blue sky and the sun gleaming on Fisher's Peak away to the east. Amid the shouts of the men playing *bocci* and the men playing *morra*, they drank beer and spoke their mother tongue. Shorty D'Ercole, an eighty-year-old ex-miner, stood with Joe "Pop" Incitti, who is seventy-five. Both are under five feet tall, both worked all their lives in the mines, and both have faces the color of the earth. They danced together in the gym, played *bocci*, and talked of old times. Shorty said to Pop, "The mules, remember the mules in the mine that was caving in? There was the lead mule, that red one with a face like a horse, in there tangled up in the chains. And I said please somebody get out the mules not for CF&I but for the animals' sake. And they were making the noise and scraping the feet and I couldn't stand it and I went in and brought them out. Then the whole thing collapsed."

Binda Cunico ran a grocery store until 1968, when the government bought him out and he and his wife Angie went to Fort Collins, where he is a butcher and she works in a grocery store. "Sopris may be the ugliest place in the world," he said, waving a beer. "But the best people got planted here."

Sixty-two-year-old Paul Butero has a warm and thoughtful face, and he talked in a quiet way of what Sopris was all about. Forty years in the mines left him with a case of black lung and there is a certain weariness in his eyes. He said, "I've lived here sixty years and the more I see the more I like it. I'd have spent the rest of my life here but . . . it's just one of those things."

Twenty-nine-year-old Joe Terry never worked in the mines. He has a master's degree and is a teacher of retarded children. "We were always poor," he said. "My dad cut up tires and put them on the soles of our shoes. He made three to five dollars a day and never saw the sun except on Sundays. They were all pick and shovel men dependent on the mules. If a mule was killed, the miner was fired. If a man was killed he was put on the cross-cut until the end of the shift. But there was always enough money to buy the grapes. As long as we had the wine we felt lucky. There is a toast we say, 'One hundred years and then you die.' And that was the way we felt."

Eighty-two-year-old Frances Furia sat in her living room, surrounded by framed photographs of her huge family. She had lived in that house for fifty-five years, the wife of a coal miner-shoemaker-barber, and the mother of twelve children. Shaking her head, wiry little Mrs. Furia snapped, "They spend millions on that dam. What advantage is it? Flood control, they say. Well, there is a house down there on the river bottom where they raised fifteen kids and I said to the engineer, how come it didn't float away? But what you going to do? Fight? Kill 'em? Then you go to jail. You argue with them, they give you less money for the house. This was a pretty camp. A band every Saturday night. I'd go outside and listen. It was like a city. Two coal mines, a coke oven, and a streetcar until they took it out and we had to walk to town like nanny goats. Oh, maybe no dam will ever come. I think they are all *pazzo* [crazy]."

When all the beer was gone, when the band stopped playing and the people began to leave, Pop Incitti went to his home in Trinidad carrying a lump of coal awarded to him for being the oldest miner at the celebration because Shorty D'Ercole went home early. He went to his cellar and drew a bottle of wine from a mound of sand; his dark eyes danced and a grin spread across his weathered face. "The wine is still good," he said. "The wine you can still make. The wine you can take with you."

The very last resident of Sopris was gone shortly thereafter, and all the houses came down and the name Sopris was omitted from the new road maps. Some of the people went out on the plains east of Trinidad and some moved north or out of the state. When they come together now they are no longer a people, but individuals living separate lives in separate places.

Sopris is a field of desolation. The dam inches its way across the river, where a 200-foot-high intake looms against the sky with the Army Corps of Engineers insignia on it and the word TRINIDAD in raised red letters. Water—some 114,500 acre feet of it—will cover not only the townsite but a massive slag heap where thousands of tons of coal tailings pose a threat of fish-killing acid. An 86-foot drawdown will leave an ugly bathtub ring of mud flats which will discourage boaters and fishermen alike, despite the Bureau of Reclamation's rosy prediction for a beautiful recreation site.

As Sopris went to its death, there was something strangely significant about the name of the river that claimed it. The early eighteenth-century massacre of a group of explorers on the river led to its being named the Purgatoire, the French translation and contraction of the Spanish El Río de las Ánimas Perdidas en Purgatorio, or the River of the Souls Lost in Purgatory. Perhaps the abandoned gravesite filled with water has the only lost souls around Sopris, or perhaps the people of Sopris feel that some part of themselves will remain forever in the river. In any case, their last wish was that the name "Sopris" be placed atop the intake tower and that the dam and reservoir be called by that name. The request was denied by the government. Within the scheme of progress, it was perhaps a foregone conclusion that although the little town of Sopris lost its life, the bigger town of Trinidad would get its name on the tombstone.

Steer riding, El Paso County Fair and Rodeo, held each August at Calhan. (Overleaf)

Pikes Peak or Bust Rodeo, held each August at the Broadmoor Hotel, Colorado Springs.

Bronc riding, El Paso County Fair and Rodeo.

Cities

Denver skyline.

IN SUMMER, the procession across the prairie is nearly bumper to bumper as thousands of cars, hot from the searing Kansas flatlands, push along Colorado's main arteries to the foothill cities of Denver, Boulder, Colorado Springs, and Pueblo. Always it is the mountains and one mountain in particular which lures the people as it did so long ago when wagons came bearing the legend, "Pikes Peak or Bust." Many did bust and turned back to their homes with a new philosophy scrawled across the boards: "Pikes Peak All a Humbug."

The words "Pikes Peak" found their way into every geography book, encyclopedia, and classroom in America, symbolizing more than just a mountain. Pikes Peak *was* the West, a place where the air was clean and life was better than anywhere else. Pikes Peak was, to millions of school children who lived at sea level, something of a heaven, nearly three miles higher than their backyards.

When the cars come in summer, Pikes Peak is a landmark visible a hundred miles away, still mystical and something of a humbug, too. The West is not Pikes Peak at all, but lies farther on, along two hundred miles of perpendicular scenery.

Pikes Peak, 14,110 feet high, from the Rampart Range Road above Cascade.

Rotunda of the State Capitol Building, Denver.

The four foothill cities have always believed the West begins at their doorstep. In those cities lives more than half of Colorado's population and, according to a city planner, "all of its faults." Smog often lies over them, stretching as much as eighty miles, especially in Denver and Pueblo. Billboards, advertising everything from funerals to pizzas, interfere with the landscape and at times even keep Pikes Peak from view. At Colorado Springs, several mile-long scars made by a concrete company digging out limestone deface the Rampart Range not far from the Air Force Academy, in plain sight of millions of motorists along Interstate 25. The cities have also been accused of complacency, lack of imagination, and what a Congregational minister calls "a case of arrested development," meaning it in a spiritual rather than physical sense.

"Every city has these faults," returns a city councilman. "We think it's awful because it's Colorado." He cites the positive aspects of the cities: clean streets and clean air at least part of the time, uncrowded, no slums, less than an hour's drive from the mountains, free roads, excellent public schools, few riots, decent housing and transportation.

The foothill cities are also some of the few places in the nation where the sun shines most of the time, a somewhat disconcerting fact for non-natives. Painter Boardman Robinson, a transplanted Easterner, stepped outside his studio after forty days of glittering skies and muttered, "This goddam sunshine."

Weather in the cities, as well as in the rest of Colorado, is usually perverse. Three feet of snow once blanketed Colorado Springs on Labor Day, causing millions of dollars' worth of damage to trees and stranding tourists in their Bermuda shorts. Another year, a hot June day ended in freezing weather and two feet of hail. In 1965, following five years of drought, the normally half-dry rivers and creeks along the foothills burst upon Denver, Colorado Springs, and Pueblo. So perplexing is the weather that forecasts occasionally get bogged down in comedy. A city newspaper once ran a weather report which began, "Fair and clear today. Could rain." A television weatherman, befuddled over a sudden cold front predicted for August, blurted over the air, "A cold mare's ass is moving down from Canada tonight." Even the weather bureau itself is sometimes uncertain. When a caller asked if it would rain in Denver that day, the meteorologist replied, "I don't know."

While the weather is part of the charm of the cities, so is their underlying lack of sophistication. Even Denver, which considers itself cosmopolitan, is still in part what eastern slicks used to call "an overgrown cow town." A Chicago woman staying at the Brown Palace told a Denverite, "People walk with their heads up here, men open doors for you, and the traffic cop

A summer afternoon at pioneer statue, Colfax and Broadway, Denver.

apologizes and calls you 'ma'am' before he gives you a ticket." A pretty ex-New York secretary now working for a Denver firm said, "The hardest thing to get used to is that if a man stops and talks to you he isn't trying to rob you or rape you. Most likely, all he wants is for you to buy a ticket to the stock show."

The naïveté that Denver tries so hard to hide surfaces quite naturally via the cowboy hat. Although the new young wizards of finance along Seventeenth Street wouldn't be caught dead in one, the cowboy hat rests comfortably on the heads of the aging chieftains of finance, business, and society. The man driving a huge Caterpillar on a road-construction job will wear one as will the brakeman on the Denver and Rio Grande Western Railroad. Cab drivers, dentists, window washers, postmen, airline pilots, real-estate salesmen and even undertakers are proud to wear that badge of western virility. When a ranch family comes into town to shop, dressed in cowboy gear from hat to boots, no one turns a hair in downtown Denver, a metropolis of well over a million people.

A hundred years ago, when other American cities already had a patina of wealth, grime, and solidarity over them, Denver was a rowdy supply point

Downtown Denver in 1959. Front Range in the distance.

and jumping off place for the diggings. To Isabella Bird, an English journalist who braved the West on horseback in 1872, Denver was a "great braggart city spread out, brown and treeless, upon a brown and treeless plain." By the time Colorado became a state in 1876, Denver had trees, wide streets, gentility, English capital, culture, and a rococo society. Gold kings replaced cattle barons and built mansions with gold-plated doorknobs, coats of arms, and chandeliers of semiprecious stones. Anyone with a foreign accent and a predilection for a title of nobility was lionized by Denver society, no questions asked. Today, nearly every Denver mansion of the nineteenth century has been turned into apartments, torn down, or sold to private clubs or cults such as the Brotherhood of the White Temple. Foreign accents are sprinkled through Denver's sports shops, bistros, condominiums, and foreign-car emporiums. Royalty still entrances society but now it may be a baron selling lipstick for a cosmetic company through a local department store.

Denver Botanic Gardens.

Left: Helen G. Bonfils, principal owner of the Denver Post, *patron of the arts, and member of historic Colorado family.*

The new Denver Art Museum, completed in 1971. (Overleaf)

Colorado Boulevard—Denver.

Around the corner from the Cootie Club, Silver Dollar Pup Tent Number 1, is one of America's finest preservations and a source of considerable Denver pride. Larimer Square, once a hangout for drunks and derelicts, is probably Colorado's most historically and architecturally significant piece of real estate. The scene of the 1858 Cherry Creek diggings, Colorado's first though unproductive gold camp, the area around Larimer Square spawned the city of Denver. Along the 1400 block of Larimer Street were Colorado's first bank, theater, art emporium, drugstore, and post office. The first assembly of Jefferson Territory met in a billiard parlor there in 1861 and five years later the first Colorado legislature convened at the same place. Architects have long considered the brick buildings of Larimer Street a prime example of Victorian architecture, complete with scallops, cornices, wrought iron, and round-topped windows.

Larimer Street reached its zenith in the 1880s and from then on began to deteriorate as elegance moved uptown. The avenue was a sleazy, shoddy area until 1963 when a young public-relations girl named Dana Crawford and her geologist husband John realized the street's potential. Backed by the money of thirteen other Larimer Square Associates, the Crawfords began the painstaking acquisition of property on both sides of the 1400 block and hired architect Langdon Morris, Jr., to recapture what they call "the Denver mystique." Morris has done his job well and there is now an intermingling

National Center for Atmospheric Research, designed by Ieōh Ming Pei, architect, Boulder.

of plazas, shops, arcades, and offices, which, though commercial, are tastefully understated. Currently under construction along Larimer Square is a vast urban-renewal project that will create an upbeat, prestigious, and superbly designed business and tourist center spread out over an eight-block former slum area.

The distance between Denver and Boulder is only twenty-seven miles, yet the difference between the two cities is enormous. Once just a lovely foothill setting for the University of Colorado, Boulder now houses the biggest conglomerate of brains in the state. Most of these are scientists and white smock technicians engaged in everything from cryogenics to the manufacture of Orbiting Solar Observatories. Where pastoral Boulder once had just two manufacturers, one making knives and hatchets and the other turning out horse hardware, it now has a dozen, including its Big Three —IBM, Ball Brothers, and Beech who together employ over five thousand people. Such heady-sounding installations as ESSA (Environmental Science Services Administration) and JILA (Joint Institute for Laboratory Astrophysics) are at Boulder, along with Neodata Services Company whose computers process subscriptions for forty-one magazines.

Boulder's most stunning complex of buildings and brains is the National Center for Atmospheric Research, atop a six-hundred-foot-high mesa which towers over a well-kept residential area and adjoins a 3500-acre city park.

United States Air Force Academy, Colorado Springs; chapel and dormitories.

An imaginative complex of new buildings variously called "a Martian pueblo," "the sun palace," and "a rose-colored ivory tower," the taut, pure citadel of pink cylinders and cubes is the only major piece of contemporary Colorado architecture which fits its mountainous surroundings. Designed by New York architect Ieoh Ming Pei, NCAR houses 350 meteorologists, astronomers, physicists, balloon engineers, and scientists who are trying to find answers to such practical problems as air pollution, modification of weather and climate, and long-term global weather prediction.

The success of the NCAR building and the spirit behind its smooth-running staff stems from Dr. Walter Orr Roberts, a pioneer in solar studies and NCAR's director. Roberts arrived in Colorado in 1940 with a wife, an ancient Graham-Paige automobile, and various parts of a coronagraph, a special solar telescope. A candidate for a Ph.D. in astronomy from Harvard, Roberts drove up to Climax, then famous only for its molybdenum mine. Roberts soon established the High Altitude Observatory, finding the rarefied air at the 11,500 foot Continental Divide thin, clear, and dry enough for him to launch his studies. He photographed, identified, and described solar spicules, relatively small jets of gas that shoot out from the edge of the sun. His research into the influence of the sun's corona and solar flares on radio communication aided Allied troops during World War II. His practical meteorology, he claims, consisted of his daily appraisal of the relative needs of the Atlantic or Pacific watershed, after which he would direct his wife to toss the dishwater out of the east or west kitchen window.

After twenty years with the High Altitude Observatory, Roberts was asked to become director of the newly formed NCAR, which was under the sponsorship of the National Science Foundation. He did not want to leave HAO nor did he want to move from Boulder where he had resided for thirteen years. He soon made HAO a division of NCAR, which stayed in Boulder because Roberts had already picked a site for it on the mesa, a view he had long admired from his living-room window.

"Without Roberts this place never would have got off the ground," says one of his co-workers. "This is one man's dream which somehow didn't get bogged down in committees and red tape. He got the state of Colorado to donate the land; he insisted on the preservation of the natural terrain on the mesa; and when it came to designing the buildings, he agreed with the architect who first of all wanted to start with some ruins."

Working closely with Pei, who designed Denver's Mile High Center, Roberts indeed "kindled to the same fire"—that of inspecting the ruins at Cortez, New Mexico, and Mesa Verde, Colorado. When Pei's first drawings turned out to be "too monolithic and we wanted it looser and more complex," Roberts sent him back to the drawing board. The building, which Roberts describes as "symbolic but not monumental, ascetic but hospitable," fits the demands of nature while complementing it. Tough enough to stand scorching sun and mesatop winds of 125 mph, the center also blends with the craggy scenery behind it. Pei and Roberts have not overlooked the fact that NCAR is a sun-oriented establishment. Sun filters through a skylight, fountains play in a reflecting pool, and short, open corridors lead to balconies and rooftop terraces. In the first floor reception area, one wall contains a twenty-foot-high photograph of the sun's corona while the wall facing it is lined with a Navajo sand painting. Two arches on the west façade provide the only incongruous note. According to one source, a draftsman for the Pei firm inserted them in the plans as he was about to leave and no one noticed them until after the contractor had done his work.

A few years ago, there was a Colorado Springs Chamber of Commerce sign on U.S. 24, the east-west approach to the city. At first it read: "Colorado Springs wants *clean* industry." Then the word *"clean"* was painted over and the second message read: "Colorado Springs wants *good* industry." A few months later *"good"* was obliterated and the sign at last proclaimed: "Colorado Springs wants *your* industry."

Colorado Springs' attitude toward industry is both quaint and appropriate for a town which has based its reputation on clear skies and a landscape

Front porch—Colorado Springs.

unmarred by giant, belching factories. Pikes Peak looms over the town, a broad-shouldered sentinel visible from nearly every avenue, and it is this image of Colorado Springs that the Chamber seeks to preserve while toying with illusions of industrial strength. Good, clean industries do exist in Colorado Springs, in handsome buildings on large tracts of land, and they manufacture complicated space-age devices. But what really enables Colorado Springs to enjoy a burgeoning economy and clear skies is not the sprinkling of industry. While tourists dump some $63,000,000 into the town annually, the military payroll is more than twice that and it is constant, unchanged by cranky weather which sometimes knocks tourism to its knees.

"Colorado Springs lusted after the military and they got it," declares one of the town's protagonists. He and other long-suffering citizens like to recall the way things were before World War II when tuberculosis and tourists supported the town. Sanatoriums, sleeping porches, and queer little t.b. houses offered respite if not cures for consumptives while well-heeled guests drank Spencer Penrose's liquor collection at the Broadmoor Hotel. The Colorado Springs of those days was gay, luxurious, and solvent. Then a

Garden of the Gods, Colorado Springs. (Overleaf)

handful of business leaders, foreseeing the eventual rupture of the beautiful life, lured the Army to town in 1940 with 35,000 free acres on which Fort Carson was built. After that came Ent Air Force Base, national headquarters of the North American Air Defense Command which is now entrenched in a one-hundred-million-dollar, virtually obsolete hole in Cheyenne Mountain. The Air Force Academy moved into its two-hundred-million-dollar complex in 1958 which some recalcitrant citizens still refer to as a "monument to too much." (Local high school students call it "the El Paso County Bird Farm.")

Many deeply rooted, past-middle-age residents tend to close their eyes to the military, excluding its economic importance as well as its cultural support and measure of urbanity. To them, "military" means the transient men in uniform who seem forever to be involved in local brawls, shootings, and car accidents and who have added to the large and unattractive sprawl of low-priced housing.

Two old friends—Colorado Springs.

The Broadmoor Hotel against Pikes Peak mas

Builders and developers take as much blame, often justified, for ruining the prewar prettiness of the town and for placing upon it the burden of change. The landgrab by military as well as developers has indeed been fantastic with little thought given to future needs of the town. A conscientious city government is torn between satisfying the demands of its building-trade and military albatross and of assuring its citizens better facilities with money the city does not have.

A power and a puzzle is the Broadmoor Hotel which rises like a pink fortress at the foot of the mountains. Visitors see it as a superelegant hostelry, offering impeccable service and accommodations which include finger bowls at breakfast, ice-water faucets in the bathrooms, and comely ladies to turn down the bedsheets. Those within say little of how the

Broadmoor is able to provide the greatest assortment of services of any hotel in America while seeming to make money doing it.

The hotel is but a small part of the El Pomar Investment Company whose assets are estimated at more than $125,000,000. Both are products of Spencer Penrose who made a fortune in Cripple Creek gold and Utah copper. Today, the El Pomar empire is run by Thayer and Russell Tutt, sons of Penrose's long-time business associate, C. L. Tutt, Jr. Both exercise com-

Broadmoor Hotel lake—Colorado Springs.

Flora Stewart, Manitou Springs pioneer at annual Buffalo Barbecue.

Shoeshine boy, Colorado Springs.

plete though judicious control over many Colorado Springs attractions including the Cheyenne Mountain Zoo, the railroads up Pikes Peak and Mount Manitou, the Will Rogers Shrine, and the well-known Pikes Peak or Bust Rodeo.

The investment company is the principal asset of the El Pomar Foundation, a great charitable institution which has given the city two libraries, a hospital, and some of its Fine Arts Center. Both Thayer and Russell Tutt are strong, behind-the-scenes leaders, who had major roles in attracting the military. An undetermined part of Colorado's political, social, and economic welfare is influenced by the Tutt brothers, whose low-keyed but dynamic voices have been raised above the prewar status quo still longed for by many Coloradoans.

Pueblo is an industrial city, suffering from polluted air and lying in a slow backwash of political, social, and economic leadership. It is, accord-

ing to an advertising man, "an unsophisticated, entrenched town with a dinner-bucket kind of philosophy." A 1960 University of Colorado survey concluded that Pueblo was strong in natural factors but had an inferiority complex. A political analyst says that Pueblo's politics "are not well-oiled enough to be called a machine. It's old-fashioned courthouse politics." A television station manager claims that "Pueblo is a place about to happen." And he may be right.

Scarcely a tourist attraction, Pueblo sits on a dusty plain, twenty-five miles from the mountains, with the Spanish Peaks looming far to the south. Its steel plant produces more than a million tons of steel per year which means that Pueblo's skyline is often dirty, reason enough for many to refer to it as "Pew-town." The state hospital and the state fair are at Pueblo, the Mafia is present but not strong, and while there are few bookstores, there is a new library. An incredible legislative coup in 1962 catapulted Pueblo's run-down two-year trade school into a fully accredited four-year state college, lodged in a set of futuristic buildings on a mesa overlooking the town.

The real chance for Pueblo to come out of its shell is the Pueblo Reservoir, a Bureau of Reclamation project scheduled for completion in 1972. The sixty-mile shoreline will give Pueblo the largest body of water along the foothills and will open the way to boating, fishing, and resort villages unknown until now. "But," says a lawyer, "Pueblo is a story of missed opportunities. They may just let somebody come in and take it away from them." Around Pueblo, optimists think not. "We're getting some pride," said one. "I haven't heard anybody say lately that Swallows (a tiny farm community scheduled to be inundated by the reservoir) ought to be saved and Pueblo flooded."

Mrs. Al Icabone, liquor-store owner, Pueblo.

John Norton, scarfer, Colorado Fuel and Iron Company, Pueblo.

Mountains

Ranch at base of Crested Butte Mountain.

THERE'S AIR OUT HERE that hasn't been breathed before."

"There's wilderness, too. I can show you some where no white man ain't never been, 'cept two, three is all. I can show it to you all right, if you got four, five days. Ain't nobody got that kind of patience though."

"Them tourists come up here with a white shirt and a ten-dollar bill and don't change neither one."

"It's a nice town. No gossip. People just don't talk about one another. Maybe they take it out in thoughts . . . I don't know."

"They used to call me the Marlboro man. I didn't mind till I saw his spurs was upside down."

How do you measure time up here?

"Well, sir, time it measures us."

They spoke as the people of the towns and the people who lived off by themselves, deep in the mountains where the winter sun leaves the east face in shadows by two o'clock in the afternoon. Life is different and yet the same for all of them, unified by the mountains which some say is their particular immortality.

Each will tell you, it's this to me: a rummage of rocks and trees and peaks and sky. A place by myself. Little things like wet grass, a caterpillar under a mushroom, rotting wood, blowing snow, mossy rock, white water,

Aerial photograph of the Spanish Peaks. West Spanish Peak (right) is 13,623 feet high; East Spanish Peak (left) is 12,683 feet high. (Overleaf)

Dr. A. C. Denman

wild iris and columbine, golden leaves trembling on an aspen tree, rainbow trout and the native cutthroat. The feeling of space, silence, melancholy, freedom, purity, and the gentle delusion that no one has ever been here before. That is only part of it. Look, they say, at the names that have been given to the mountains: Slippery Sides, Fools, Terrible, Iron Clad, Coffin, Mummy, Little Scraggly, Schoolmarm, Prohibition, Expectation, Bandit, and Hunchback. Passes called Slumgullion, Gunsight, Breakneck, Blowout, Hardscrabble, and Son-of-a-Bitch. Creeks that have such names as Starvation, Troublesome, O' Be Joyful, Opposition, Poison, Horse Thief, Weary Man, Stinking Water, Dirty Woman, and Fourth of July. There are gulches called Slaughterhouse, Poverty, Hog John, and Jackass. There are Calamity and Sewemup Mesas, No Good Park and Skinny Fish Lake. Names born of frustration, hope, irony, and a sense of humor. Behind the names the mountains and behind the mountains an enigma. No one can know all of it and even those who were born and raised in the mountains will sometimes say that all they know is where they came from.

Ernie West, Cripple Creek; a former welterweight champion.

Above: Dr. Denman with patient at Hilltop Hospital, Cripple Creek.

Right: Café owner, Victor. This is the only café now open in this old mining town.

Dr. Denman and Ernie West receive bad news on a Cripple Creek street.

Dr. Denman and rancher Lew Altman meet at gas station, Cripple Creek.

Sixty million years ago when the aged earth was still shuddering and shaking from the ordeal of its birth, the Rockies were squeezed, folded, and shoved out from the very bowels of the planet. The folds overturned and split, whole mountains cracked and burst into flame, creating rich ores out of the holocaust. Then slowly the molten earth cooled and water ran down its heaving flanks, forming rivers which scarred the mountain face even more. Receding seas left snails and sharks' teeth in the shale beds while ferns and tiny fish became souvenirs of forest turned to stone. Wind and water continued to eat at the mountains and then at last a sheet of ice covered them and began to melt, leaving behind the U-shaped valleys, moraines, and cup-shaped cirques of a mountain personality.

Above all this the peaks stood out, unbearably white, oblivious to time and season. When man finally came, he was an Indian and the mountains gave him shelter, food, and spirit, and that was enough. It remained for the white man to assault the mountains and the Indians. For a time the odds were with the mountains and the aboriginals who understood and respected them. The conquistadors were turned back and so were the padres. But when the beaver hat appeared in London in 1799, there was no turning back as trapper after trapper discovered the high country. Confronted with a vast, untamed wilderness, the trappers defied the brutality of the mountains and negated every emotion except that of conquest. As space swallowed them and loneliness cut into them as deeply as the gorges and river beds from which they took their beaver, the trappers pitted themselves against the raw land and overcame its every obstacle. Again and again the Indians struck them down but the trappers, better armed and infused with cold determination, fought back with a cruelty unmatched by the savages they sought to annihilate. By 1840, the streams were stripped of beaver by the mountain men who also knew every last crevice, valley, and ridge which could hide an Indian. They led armies to them and settlers past them and then rode out to slaughter the buffalo on the plains. The trappers were the link between the new land and the homesick people and they became a kind of unchallenged god and prophet. But none of them foresaw the day when the mountains would pour forth a treasure greater than all the beaver pelts they had ever imagined.

From 1859 when George Jackson made the first big strike at the junction of Chicago and Clear Creeks until long after big strike of the century, the mountains bled gold and silver in drops and spurts gouged out by a new kind of maniac—the prospector. Scrambling over cliffs and precipices which had discouraged the trappers, the prospectors pushed higher and higher along the ridges, striking it rich at Central City, Tarryall, Buckskin Joe, Breckenridge,

St. Elmo, Tincup, Fairplay, Leadville, Aspen, Silver Cliff, Rosita, and hundreds of little camps which played out overnight. The same high, thin cry of the wilderness lured trapper and prospector alike. Neither respected nature, neither found comfort in riches but both recognized a certain fulfillment in the lonely, perilous trails they followed. The difference between them was that the trappers were fewer in number and the effects of their plunder scarcely disturbed the land. By the time the prospectors spilled over to Crested Butte, Ouray, Telluride, Creede, and finally Cripple Creek in 1891, the insides of the mountains stood in heaps and around them the mangle grew worse. Rivers were poisoned by mill tailings, people dropped from dysentery, small pox, scarlet fever, and diphtheria. Refuse was pitched out the door beside animal excrement and the remains of butchered animals left in the streets to rot. The little narrow-gauge trains groaned up the slopes with supplies occasionally carrying luxuries such as fresh meat and dried fruit which prompted one boardinghouse keeper to post a sign: "Any

Cripple Creek: Top of abandoned mine shaft called "gallows frame." Sangre de Cristo Mountains sixty miles away.

man who won't eat prunes is a son-of-a-bitch."

The little camps are all gone now and the ore houses are silent and the gallows frames are crumbling against the empty hillsides. Not a trace remains of Bugtown, Royal Flush, Gassy, Whiskey Park, Poverty Flats, Kokomo, or hundreds like them. Others, like Holy Cross City, Independence, East Willow, and Anaconda are nearly back to nature and it is difficult to tell where their rotting timbers leave off and the earth begins. Gothic, St. Elmo, Romley, Vicksburg, Winfield, and Ninety Four have almost reached ghost-town status although the real-estate boom is reviving some of them for people who place nostalgia before an indoor toilet. The best of the gold camps—Cripple Creek, Aspen, Central City, Creede, Telluride, Ouray, Crested Butte, and Silverton—have succumbed to varying degrees of tourism, yet the effects of time and vanished man hangs over all of them. The gap between then and now is truly shorter in these places where the essence of Colorado manages to creep through.

Above: Abandoned hut at the northern end of the San Luis Valley near Villa Grove. Sangre de Cristo Mountains in background.

Left: Holy Cross City, just under 11,000 feet, in the Sawatch Mountains. These two buildings are all that is left of a mining town that was deserted by 1883.

Telluride, still-active mining town. Black Bear jeep road in background.

In the southwestern part of Colorado is the state's biggest concentration of towering, jagged peaks over 14,000 feet high which seems to preclude any essence save that of incompatibility. Yet deep within that two-hundred-square-mile area are three inhabited towns—Silverton, Ouray, and Telluride—which fill in the gap between then and now. Of these, Telluride is the most remote, astonishingly beautiful, and marked with a hard-bitten stillness. Although only six miles of mountains separate Ouray and Telluride, the distance by paved road is fifty. Two terrifying jeep roads go to the town and three hundred miles of tunnels from a lead, zinc, and silver mine eventually exit above the main street. Thirteen-thousand-foot-high Ajax Mountain looms directly behind Telluride and down its craggy face bursts Bridal Veil Falls, dropping nearly four hundred feet. Close to the falls is a zigzag jeep road and a miners' boardinghouse, deserted now although the mine still operates. Almost forty feet of snow falls on Telluride each year, some of it as late as the middle of June. So rugged and wild is this area that named avalanches roar down both sides of the canyon in spring, causing the surviving trees to grow horizontally.

Canyon of the Lodore along the Green River in northwestern Colorado.

Once a teeming mining camp of five thousand people, Telluride's population has dwindled to three hundred, "including some mountain goats." The bank is now the Elks Hall and most of the false-fronted stores have been closed for years in spite of signs on them which read "open all night," "please ring buzzer," and "we never close." There is one small motel, a couple of cafés, and no tourist attractions except jeep tours and a sometime melodrama in the Sheridan Hotel. Toughened by the elements and bred to a life that seeks no favors, the people of Telluride are used to inconvenience and make much of digging out each spring. They seem to feel that theirs is a world apart, enriched by one another and made special by solitude. "And I can tell you," said a service-station attendant, "that we got so much altitude here that nobody writes nothing dirty on the washroom walls."

Over the divide from Telluride, not far from the headwaters of the Rio

Lumbermen playing cards in the Pagosa Springs Hotel lobby. (Overleaf)

Grande, is the only town in Mineral County. Creede, like Telluride, is away from the throng, almost hidden between two canyon walls, and virtually unspoiled. The town's only hotel is almost always filled with miners who straggle in at odd hours, carrying lunchboxes, wearing hard hats with lights attached, and usually in need of a shave. They dig out silver, lead, and zinc at the Emperious Mine and come from their black and lonesome trade with their heads up, zooming down the narrow canyon road from the mountain in jeeps, trucks, and dusty cars. They drink straight whisky at the hotel bar, laugh much, and on Saturday nights when a lumberjack comes in to play the square grand, dance with each other if there are no women around. There are several other saloons along Creede's main street and they hit them all, playing the pinball machines, and drinking more whisky under the solemn stares of the deer and elk heads on the walls. The miners, and

Below: Wood and tool sheds—Crested Butte.

Mrs. Lensch and friend, Westcliffe.

a few summer tourists who may have to share the bathroom with them, keep the old Creede Hotel going but even so the woman who owns it is disheartened. Her son, postmaster by day and bartender by night comes in and she says to him, "I'm ready to trade it off for a yellow dog." But she doesn't really mean it. Creede has got under her skin, too.

"Tourism gives us a shot in the arm so we can face the winter," says a man at the bar who runs an air compressor in the mine. "Gets thirty-nine below. Then spring comes and we find ourselves looking up the ass end of an avalanche pret' near every day." But tourism in Creede simply means a melodrama by the Creede Metropolitan Opera Company; windswept Boot Hill where plastic flowers adorn the grave of Bob Ford, Jesse James' murderer who was shot in his Creede saloon; and West Willow, a mile up the

Musicians warming up for an outdoor dance and picnic in the forest up Cement Creek. Families are from nearby Crested Butte, an eastern European mining community beginning to thrive on the current land, ski, and see boom.

creek, scene of crumbling shacks and an ore bucket hung on a cable a thousand feet straight up.

There is no doctor, dentist, or policeman in Creede. The firehouse is orange and the old plank jail is almost back to nature. This was a town of gunfights, lynchings, and gambling where Bat Masterson, Soapy Smith, Slanting Annie, and Poker Alice became infamous. But there is not too much talk of those things in Creede anymore. The proprietress of the hotel says they are waiting for a new silver boom and produces a list of mining claims: the Baritone Wonder, Give a Damn, Great Relief, Glass Eye, Hope and Doubt, Neversweat, and the Kreutzer Sonata. "It's so," says a little old lady all dressed in gold from head to foot. "Used to be a prospector myself in Gilpin County. Smells like prosperity around here again."

In Cripple Creek, a hundred miles northeast, no one speaks of prosperity. The mining rebirth prophesied for other old towns has not aroused much enthusiasm here. This is a town revitalized only in the summer when more than twenty thousand visitors stream around the backside of Pikes Peak and down into the crater which holds Cripple Creek. The attraction is the Imperial Hotel and the oldest operating melodrama in the country, produced six nights a week for three months of the year. "When the hotel shuts down we don't die, we decline," says an antique dealer. Nonetheless, out of season Cripple Creek is a town blatantly itself, not quite hospitable, not quite dead, not quite forgotten.

Along the main street, most of the buildings are gradually falling down. Great swatches of wallpaper flap against the brick underneath; birds nest in attic windows; and wind rushes through the carcasses of the old places. Sometimes cattle nibble on grass growing inside the buildings while outside the sidewalks are buckling. On the sides of buildings are old and faded signs for the *Denver Post*, the undertaker, and the livery stable. A few places are open for food and drink and tires and municipal government. Down the street is the Teller County courthouse and the jail—solid, Victorian, and virtually empty.

Cripple Creek somehow does not convey stagnation or desperation or even much sadness. It leaves one with the feeling of having just looked back, of a hand stuck in still-warm history. What was there is still there—the gingerbread houses, the pock-marked hillsides, the ore houses and gallows frames, the bits of villages in nearly every gulch—ghosts, yes, but noble ones. What rises from the ruin are the miners, the boardinghouse keepers, the merchants, the doctors, and the little people who lived and worked in the District, as it was called, and who still live there, a mélange of first- and second-generation Cripple Creekers.

Ski lodge, Crested Butte ski area. German Language Club from Denver is introducing local cowpunchers to European dances.

Old medicine bottles in Springer's Drugstore, Central City.

The last of the great mining camps, Cripple Creek was a cattle pasture until 1890 when gold was discovered along Poverty Gulch. Twelve towns sprang up in the twenty-four-square-mile district and the population swelled to 50,000. During the next half-century such mines as the Cresson, Portland, Anaconda, and Independence figured in the total of $380 million worth of ore which found its way out of the area around Tenderfoot Hill. The last operating mine, the Mollie Kathleen, expired in 1962 when the Carlton Mill finally shut down and the population shrank to 500.

The miners remember those days not so much with glory but with recollections of sunless days, respiratory disease, and wages which brought them neither wealth nor independence. Too old and too poor now to move, these people would refuse to go even if they had the means. No one bothers them much, except to gawk, and they can sit on their porches and watch the sun go down behind the distant Sangre de Cristos. "It's clean here," said one, "and ain't nobody in a hurry. I can do what I want. Last week I was going to plant a patch of potatoes . . . but I didn't."

The town of Meeker had no gold or silver boom. Its legacy is evolving now. A dentist who moved there from Colorado Springs calls it "a place between where people go." The town, named for the arrogant Indian agent Nathan Meeker who was murdered there by Utes in 1879, lies in the sweeping White River Valley where the mountains end and the land begins to shrivel into the canyon and mesa country. No scheduled airline stops at Meeker and there is no train and no bus except the Wilderness Transportation Company which stops on its way between Grand Junction and Craig. Meeker does not lie within forty miles of a major highway and the two state routes which pass through it do so almost indifferently. There are a couple of small motels and the old Meeker Hotel where elderly men often sit under the elk and deer heads swapping stories and talking about such things as a ten-day sheep drive into Utah or somebody's horse which slipped off the trail into a ravine.

This is a town of beat-up cowboy hats and mud-caked boots, of pickup trucks, jeeps, and unlocked automobiles, of living pioneers who came as long ago as 1882 and millionaires who have come only recently and bought huge ranches. There is talk of an oil-shale boom and a dam along the White River but few seem to want to trade privacy for progress. By no means a backward town, Meeker has a municipal pool, a new high school, vital church and civic groups. Most residents, however, recognize the town as one of the last frontiers, a place of serenity and hard work, of few tourists and no veneer.

Villains and heroes in melodrama at the Imperial Hotel, Cripple Creek.

Bennett Avenue, Cripple Creek.

Above: Dining room of the Gus Center home, Central City.

Right: Eureka Street in snowstorm, Central City.

Meeker is also a town of simple humanness. When a Meeker woman driving a mail route between there and Vernal, Utah, was thrown out of her truck and killed, the Meeker *Herald* ran her obituary on the front page, closing with the sentiment, "She leaves to cherish her memory, in addition to her husband and eight children, all of Meeker."

And then, too, there is a peculiar independence in people around Meeker. When a coyote and mountain-lion trapper quit camp suddenly, his boss called after him, "Hey, Joe, what's the matter?" Without turning, the trapper replied, "The pancakes wasn't round."

No one knows his name much beyond Meeker and Rio Blanco County and what he does will never make history. Yet Bob Hilkey, a gentle trapper, guide, and horseshoer is himself the wilderness, a remnant of things past, and a symbol of what ought to be preserved.

One day in late fall he rode along a trail beside dark and tumbling Marvine Creek, a clear, eternally cold stream which begins at about 10,500 feet in the Flattops Primitive Area, some thirty miles southeast of Meeker. Hunting season was over, yet Hilkey, dressed in a battered hat and bluejean jacket, watched constantly for elk, training his eye on the dense forest which edged within a hundred yards of the creek. His horse stood motionless, his cigaret was pressed between his fingers, and then he hooted toward the trees, a strange, nasal cry which echoed along the deserted path and snow-patched

Colt along White River Valley near Buford.

Bob Hilkey.

slopes. All at once five elk, four cows and a bull, stepped into a snowy clearing and raised their heads in the direction of Hilkey who called again and then fell silent, watching the animals as they ran into the forest, and steam rose from the snow where they had been standing.

Farther along the trail where it climbs into a broad meadow and becomes easy for a while, Hilkey stopped again, this time beside a beaver pond fringed with ice. Out of the deep pool a head appeared, then a body, and then a great tail which slapped the water and disappeared. Hilkey pointed out the beaver's house with its little room for drying feet, and the pile of winter food, and the half-gnawed aspen about to fall across the trail. He looked a long time at what the beaver had done and at the dark head which appeared once more and he said, "The Forest Service wants to eliminate beaver. They don't know it's impossible. You trap out a creek one fall and next spring they come from someplace else. So me, when I trap, I take maybe half of what's there and leave the rest for next year. Balances the whole thing out."

The snow was drifted across the trail in places, deep enough that the horses went slowly, breathing steam into the crisp air. The creek was half

Spruce trees on a hillside, midwinter, San Juan Mountains.

Elk family.

Rocky Mountain jay, commonly called a camp robber.

iced yet grass still grew in places along the bank where the sun had burned through the snow. There was no sound except the desperate thrust of wind cutting through the trees, the almost imperceptible drop of snow sloughing off the south side of rocks and hillocks, Steller's jays shrieking from the spruce trees and Hilkey's dog breathing hard beside the horses. Ahead, two lakes named Marvine, Upper and Lower, the color of sapphires, but changing with the light to amber and finally to slate. Hushed, solemn, still, populated by itinerant ducks and permanent beaver, the lakes sit in craters. On one side a sheer rock wall rises five hundred feet or more, on the other is a lava field and gentle forested slopes with trails going to even more inaccessible wilderness.

Walton Creek near Steamboat Springs, Yampa River Basin.

Westcliffe, in the Wet Mountain Valley, a railroad boom town of the 1880s. Sangre de Cristo Mountains in background. The school is abandoned, the church still in use. The name of the town is misspelled on the school building.

For a time Hilkey was one with the wilderness, off by himself, saying nothing to anyone, riding alone up the mountain, to the very top, and down again. Then he sat by the fire, drinking brandy, watching the ducks. "One spring," he said, "I saw a funny thing there where the creek empties into the lake. A water ouzel started building a nest in a hollow log in the middle of the stream. And every afternoon, because it was spring, the snow came melting off the mountain and ran into the stream. Every afternoon the water rose a little more and almost covered the log. But the bird kept working and the water kept rising more and more and pretty soon it was covering the nest. One morning I went out and she'd laid an egg and I knew right off the water'd take it that afternoon. I walked around wondering what to do. If I moved the nest she'd never go back to the egg. If I left it there it'd wash away. So I sat down and waited, looking at the water ouzel and her at me. But that afternoon the water never rose. You can't tell me that bird didn't know the water wasn't going to rise the day she laid her egg."

Along the trail, Marvine Lakes area.

Line camp of Guy Cook, an old-time cowboy who spends his summers along Miller Creek, east of Meeker.

Early each spring when the snow is still on the ground, Hilkey sets off for the Piceance Creek Basin which people around there pronounce "Pee-ants." The area is about the size of New Jersey and is virtually uninhabited except for an isolated ranch or two. Within that vastness roams the last wild horse herd in Colorado, said to number 200 head. According to legend and the best of Meeker knowledge, the horses are descendants of mustangs left by the Utes when they were banished to Utah following the Meeker massacre. The country where the horses live is as wild and desolate as any in the West, covered with bluffs, cedar-sage washes and gullies "big enough to put a house in." Threatened by cattle and sheep men who hold grazing permits in the area, the wild horses are also endangered by horsemeat buyers and by the fencing of government land which will cut them off from water. Many also die from "winter kill"—sub-zero temperatures and heavy snow.

Newborn wild colt, separated from his mother, is carried home by rancher in Piceance Creek Basin.

For years Hilkey's springtime ritual with his long-time rancher friend Minford Beard has been to rope, if luck is with them, one or two wild studs which they later use as saddle horses. Sometimes they spend a week tracking the creatures through the snow only to have the stronger, surer-footed wild horses outrun them and disappear into the heavy brush. If a mare is caught, she is turned loose. Once foaling starts, Hilkey and Beard return home until the following year. "These old studs aren't worth much—maybe thirty-five dollars is all," says Hilkey. "So why do we kill ourselves to get one? I guess because it's one of the things you can still do that's between you and nature."

Bob Hilkey and helper shoeing horses at Guy Cook's cabin.

*Jeep road across tributary of Homestake Creek, near Mount of the
Holy Cross, Sawatch Mountains. Elevation here approximately 10,000 feet.*

Sometimes Hilkey looks to the distant mountains and says, "I wish I had lived a hundred years ago but I wouldn't want to be alive a hundred years from now. You imagine yourself rough and tough. You imagine you could've been a hand in those days. That's all it is, you know . . . this wilderness stuff."

The wilderness has its own mortality in spite of furious efforts by the Colorado Open Space Foundation, an award-winning group which has helped break the state's apathy toward conservation. Primitive areas such as the Gore Range-Eagles Nest are constantly threatened by road builders, politicians, and special interest groups. An ex-Colorado governor urged a route through almost seven thousand acres of that primitive area on the grounds that people who had never seen wilderness before could go right through it by car. The state's AAA also favored a road, arguing that motels and restaurants would benefit. After several years of debate, the proposed road was vetoed by Secretary of Agriculture Orville Freeman who scored the state's "highway mentality."

Highway mentality and change are indeed upon the mountains in a curious dichotomy of wanting the West to remain exactly as it is and pressing to make every square mile of it profitable. Developers from Colorado and almost every American metropolis have cast appraising eyes at the mountains and envisioned a greater yield than the fur trade and prospecting put together. Quite literally in the middle of nowhere armies of bulldozers have cleared forests and sides of mountains and over their din is heard at every turn the cry of "recreation" and, in softer tones, "profit." With the upsurge of skiing and now the reservoirs, Colorado highways are heavy with slat-carrying automobiles in winter and choked with campers in summer. "Everybody wants the goddamn wilderness," declares a Colorado architect who retreats to Wyoming these days. "There ain't none. Listen for a lark bunting and all you hear is a cash register."

Less acid but no less sincere in their dismay are people who have always lived in the open spaces. While some have reluctantly sold great chunks of their domain to developers, others are just as determined to die in the kinnikinnick if need be to keep all outsiders away. One rancher has erected a sign on U.S. 24 as it runs through his property at South Park, an almost uninhabited, nearly treeless plain about a hundred square miles in size. The sign reads: "No Loitering." On a deserted highway toward Wetmore, another rancher has placed this warning: "Anyone discarding Kleenex will be shot." Others are annoyed with the Bureau of Reclamation for building or planning to build dams on every major Colorado river. One, discovering that the Fryingpan-Arkansas project called for a dam near his property,

Twiggy, a four-week-old fawn gently mothered by the entire staff of park rangers at Great Sand Dunes National Monument.

Picnic in the Tarryall Mountains.

Cattle drive out of the White River Valley to the Flattops near Meeker.

protested to his congressman that he had come to Colorado for the dryness and was convinced the dam would raise the humidity. But for most Coloradoans, vast reservoirs such as Dillon near Frisco, John Martin near Las Animas, and Blue Mesa at Gunnison mean fishing and boating heretofore confined to Twin Lakes, Eleven Mile, Granby, Grand Lake, and dozens of smaller ones. Membership in boat, country, and ski clubs is *de rigueur* for newly arrived young executives who also may be speculators in everything

Summertime, Aspen. (Overleaf)

Fishing camp, White River Plateau near Meeker.

from unborn mountain resorts to duck-hunting preserves. A mountain retreat, whether a condominium, a quarter-of-a-million-dollar chalet at Vail, or an old miner's cabin, is considered one of life's necessities if not one of its better investments.

Though its days grow short, the wilderness seems immortal even yet, especially in spring when catkins drip from aspen and ranchers who hold grazing permits in the national forests move their cattle on three- and four-day drives from winter pasture near their ranches to new grass in the alpine meadows. They make a gala affair of it, with women and children helping, as well as men from neighboring ranches, some of whom ride along for a day or so and then go home. Nightly cow camps are usually set up along back-country roads not far from the cattle trail and are furnished by truckloads of supplies from ranch headquarters. This is a different sort of roughing it than in the old days but the elements of solitude and mountain vastness are still there. On these drives, a man can still ride for days without sign of habitation or another human being, except perhaps a rotting cabin or sagging fence. And he has time to notice things: steam rising from the cattle's backs soon after the sun comes up; a cow pausing to have

Snowshoes and blue spruce.

*Timberline, battleground for trees struggling to survive at 11,000
feet, near top of Hermit Pass in the Sangre de Cristo Mountains.*

her calf on the trail; a coyote run into an arroyo, roped, and released;
the young boys making a contest of roping the cattle's hoofs; the warmth of
the day filtering through the trees and feeling good on the back. In the
sloppy ground are the beginnings of sunflowers, marsh marigolds, skunk
cabbage, columbine, and false hellebore, tentative among aspen so remote
that no one has yet carved his initials on the trunks.

On one of these drives, an old man and his dog rode out from a line
shack and the old man said a little sadly, "Life is so daily nowadays."
Plumb tired he was, he said, and what's the use of working so hard when

"they's only one night between two days." The old man tore a piece off a plug of Brown's Mule Tobacco and squirted the juice into a patch of lingering snow and rode back down the mountain without saying goodbye. One of the cowboys said the old man was almost eighty now, used to drive steers all the way from Mexico to Wyoming.

At the end of the day, when the cowboys wilted a little and deer came to drink in a stream by the edge of the camp, somebody said, "They's strength in trees. Laying out here at night with the wind comin' through the trees it's not so lonesome. Trees, they kind of talk." And another man said, "There's four smells I like. Pitchwood, gun oil, the forest after it rains, and horse manure." Nobody laughed at any of it. They stirred the fire, threw cold water on top of the coffee to settle the grounds, watched the horses munching the hay brought up in the truck, and listened to the wings of a night hawk beating against the air as he flew low. The sky pressed down on the clearing and the last of the sun turned the clouds orange. Then the Milky Way appeared, seemingly tossed upon the sky not too far above. Except for the camp, there was not a single light in any direction, nor any man-made sound or smell or object. Someone said, "They must have seen it same as this, a long time ago." Only the dogs, barking nervously toward the trees, said it wasn't so.

But the wilderness is not compatible with man for very long with one notable exception. All along and across those mountains, tucked away in rain-soaked meadows and quiet glens are the strangest of all Westerners—the sheepherders. Some are Basque and some are Greek and others are Navajo or Spanish-American; most are old, a few are young; all live isolated, lonely lives away from mankind and the barest thread of civilization. They are found everywhere in the high country, their places marked by wagons resembling a metal Conestoga or by tents when the terrain becomes too rugged for wagons. Sometimes they go mad from loneliness or from lightning which smothers the mountaintops and literally stands their hair on end. For months at a time they live without contact with society, speaking only to the man who comes once or twice a month with supplies. Sometimes they hide from him because they cannot bear the touch.

Near Telluride, a Navajo sheepherder named Shaggy is on the move every four or five days, sometimes with a wagon but more often with a tent. Even in summer there is likely to be snow at 11,000 feet and ripping winds which blow against the canvas and the mud banked up around it. At night Shaggy never really sleeps for he knows that sheep offer little resistance to coyotes, disease, and weather. So he listens and hears the sheep crying and knows it is too late. He is up at dawn, finding three sheep

Joe Chacon, a sheepherder at Livingston's Ranch near the Thornburgh Battleground south of Craig.

Aguilar Cemetery and Spanish Peaks, 12,683 and 13,623 feet high.

Manuel, a Spanish-American sheepherder.

dead, another with its back end eaten away, yet standing there trying to eat. He gathers them together by rattling a string of beer cans and tries to count how many are left but he can only count to fifteen. He goes back to his tent and cooks breakfast—coffee, bacon, and camp bread—a thin, hard biscuit. Afterward, he drags the dead sheep far away from the rest and plants them with strychnine, remembering his canvas gloves with a hole in one finger. He is careful this time for last month his dog got on to the poison and his boss has not had time to bring him a new one. A little more lonesome now but he does not notice. His mind is on

Sheepherder with his flock in South Park.

the sheep. Twenty per cent of the flock will die before the season ends from old age, coyotes, poison plants, and wandering off.

Twenty miles from Shaggy's camp is that of Manuel, an elderly Spanish-American who resembles a cheerful *santo*. Manuel lives in a tiny wagon furnished with a wood stove, a bed nailed crosswise in the wagon, and built-in seats which double as storage space. On the wall is a small mirror, a Carmelite mission calendar with the days marked off and two pictures of Jesus. A wind-up clock runs fifteen minutes slow. Stashed along the shelves are potatoes, flour, lard, cornmeal, salt pork, a rifle with a piece missing, fifty pounds of dog meal, and two containers of kerosene. There is a wash basin and worn but clean towels along one wall. Outside are his water jugs and a butchered sheep hanging from a tree. Manuel has a wife and family in New Mexico whom he visits twice a year. The rest of the time he is with the sheep, not lonely he says, but away from things which make him unhappy.

A third herder lives in the same vast, rugged, and unpredictable country. He was a shy, quiet man who hid from strangers until one summer when he rode into the tiny town of Dunton and announced he'd emptied his .22 into three women at his camp. The news was broadcast by the nearest radio station and police moved quickly to the scene of the crime. But all they found was a kettle which had boiled dry and the spent shells from his gun. The herder, they reported, was deathly afraid of women and imagined three of them had come to get him.

All three herders work for Fred Cline, Jr., a third generation sheepman who lives on a hill overlooking Dolores, an old and unfettered town in an exquisite setting along the river of the same name. Cline's roots go back to the 1870s when his great-grandfather was an ox freighter between Monte Vista and Rico. His grandfather, a part-time Indian fighter, drove the first herd of sheep into the Dolores area shortly after 1900. Rich in land but poor in profits, Cline says he will be out of the sheep business by 1972, citing a shortage of labor, poor prices for sheep, and rising taxes as spelling his doom. "My trouble is I didn't go to college," he says gloomily, wondering what he will do with himself. Many sheepmen near Dolores have already sold out or are going into the cattle business instead. But Cline cannot quite tear himself away from sheep, in spite of the fact that he is allergic to wool and eats all other meat except lamb. "You get used to sheep," he says. "It's all I've ever done."

Forty years ago Cline might have been out of the sheep business for other reasons. The celebrated range wars between sheep and cattle men which began early in the century lasted until 1934 when the Taylor Grazing Act put 142,000,000 acres of open range in the public domain under the supervision of what eventually became the Bureau of Land Management. Before the Taylor Grazing Act, bitter cattlemen slaughtered sheep by the thousands, threatened, mauled, and even murdered sheepmen who eventually got an edge on the cattlemen and their overgrazed rangeland. But even though the range wars were a long time ago and grazing permits assure fair disbursement of public land, resentment still exists between many sheep and cattle men. One cattleman insists his herd won't drink where sheep have drunk "because they can't stand the aroma." Another says grimly that

Sheepman Bud Cline and son.

Portrait of revered bull on barn near Gunnison, heart of the registered Hereford ranches.

"there's two things wrong with this country—the Game Department and sheep. Can't do much about the one, but t'other—well, know why we don't kill rattlesnakes or coyotes out here? The coyotes kill the sheep and the rattlesnakes might bite the sheepherder."

"Welcome to Hayden, a well-blessed community," says the sign on U.S. 40 as it parallels the Yampa River not far from Steamboat Springs. Behind Hayden's self-analysis is Farrington Carpenter, the first U. S. Director of Grazing under the Taylor Grazing Act who would rather be known for what he has done for Hayden. In his eighties now, Carpenter lives on his ranch at Hayden where he still works long hours with his cattle and reminisces every now and then about what it was like when the stagecoach ran from Wolcott in 1905 when he first arrived.

"This part of Colorado was mostly settled up by bachelors," he recalls. "There was a terrible shortage of she-stuff. Up at Elkhead, where I was homesteading and had the beginnings of a cattle herd, there wasn't a woman within miles except a fine old pioneer lady named Mrs. Murphy and she was happily married to Mr. Murphy."

Carpenter has a long, weather-beaten face which breaks into a grin when he starts his matter-of-fact storytelling. He is a graduate of Princeton University and the Harvard Law School and he came out to Colorado, he says, "all filled with that social reform that I'd got under Woodrow Wilson at Princeton. I wanted to build a schoolhouse but unfortunately there wasn't a child within miles and the law said we needed ten. We rocked along for several years until 1913 when the railroad came to town. This brought in a flood of homeseekers looking for 'free land.' One day I went in town and ran into a man who looked discouraged: I asked him what his trouble was and he said he didn't know what he was going to do. He couldn't find suitable land to file on for a homestead and he hadn't a cent and there was his wife and eleven children back in Michigan. Eleven children, I said, what ages? Four to twenty, he said. Welcome to Elkhead, brother, I told him. We will show you a homestead and plow you out an irrigation ditch and give you a milk cow. I went to my partner and said, 'the Lord has heard our prayers and here is a man with eleven head.'"

The schoolhouse built, Carpenter advertised in the East for high-caliber college graduates to staff it. Each was required to submit a recent photograph which the bachelors would tack up on the wall, making their selection based on the comeliness as well as the intelligence of the young ladies. That fall, two arrived and were married in the spring and so it went until every bachelor at Elkhead had a wife, including Carpenter. His first wife died in 1957 and he later married the first schoolteacher who had come out in 1916 and was widowed some years later.

The first graduating class at Elkhead High totaled seven. "Every one of those sagebrush kids went on to college and had outstanding careers," boasts Carpenter. What he does not say is that he established a scholarship fund for them to go. When the homesteaders finally gave up on the untamed land and the school closed, Carpenter organized the Hayden Union High School, the first consolidated school in the state. He saw that there was a swimming pool, decent salaries for teachers, and a physical education department because "when in the Army in World War One, I noticed that country boys were not coordinated like city boys who had had supervised sports and gym work." The Boy Rangers (boys eight to twelve years old), which he headed for twenty-two years he considers his "most lasting contribution" because "I had those kids every Thursday night and could see I was doing some good."

Carpenter also engineered a sewerage system, a public library, and a hospital for Hayden. For years he offered to write a will free for anyone wishing to make a donation of a dollar or more to the hospital. So persuasive was he, however, that ranchers ended up leaving a good deal more than they intended to the hospital where Carpenter served as secretary-treasurer for twenty-seven years.

As a lawyer and one-time district attorney for three counties, Carpenter prosecuted horse thieves, cattle rustlers, and bank robbers, working almost singlehandedly out of an eight- by forty-five-foot-long office in Hayden which had once been a one-lane bowling alley. As D.A. he published yearly reports in the newspapers, an unheard of practice which listed such offenses as altering brands, driving scabby sheep on the highway, possession of elks' teeth, and larceny of livestock.

"I remember the first case I ever had," recalls Carpenter. "A railroad condemnation case. The D.A. came up to me afterward and said, 'the worst thing was the way you talked to the jury. You talked like you were addressing a thousand people. Pick out what looks to be the weakest-minded SOB and go over and start talking to him in a conversational tone. When you see he's satisfied with your case, go on to the next one.' I said to him, 'how do you tell?' He told me that when a man listens to another man talk and is greatly interested, his neck starts coming out of his collar. I took his advice and stretched a lot of necks before I was through."

A lifelong Republican, Carpenter served one term in the state legislature and was appointed State Director of Revenue, reorganizing the tax system

Farrington Carpenter.

so efficiently that it is still in use. "But unfortunately I organized myself out of politics for good," he says with a wink.

He is proud of the fact that he was director of three things and was fired from every one. He failed to be reappointed by a new governor "who wanted to make a political plum of the job of Director of Revenue." As Director of Development for Denver University he was replaced because "they wanted faster results than I thought was advisable." As U. S. Director of Grazing, however, Carpenter was up against a whole bureaucracy and the Secretary of the Interior, Harold Ickes. Carpenter circumvented the bureaucracy by letting the stockmen apportion the range themselves, a method which was quick, fair, and unorthodox. The act became self-regulating and because of the small fee charged for grazing, self-supporting. So well did the scheme work that at the end of the first year Carpenter returned to the Treasury Department nearly half his annual budget of $240,000. This was the ultimate heresy and Ickes tried for the next three years to have Carpenter fired, only to be thwarted by Congressman Taylor, author of the act, and President Roosevelt. When Carpenter finally resigned, certain that the stockman were so self-regulating that Ickes would not interfere, "Ickes reluctantly gave me a letter of satisfactory services and called after me as I left the room, 'you're out of a job, you're out of a job, you're out of a job.'"

Carpenter has ranked among the West's top cattlemen for years and his registered, purebred Herefords bring consistently high prices. Only once in his long career were Carpenter's cattle threatened with oblivion. "In the early days when we ran our cattle on the unfenced open range, a neighbor's short-horn bull kept getting in with our heifers and creating mottle-faced calves. We had two choices—either get rid of the bull or go out of the registered purebred cattle business. Nobody wanted to kill the bull outright so we thought of a plan. My partner had a mother who doted on him—was always sending him things for his cabin he couldn't use. She'd sent these glass doorknobs and so one day we roped that old bull, stretched him out at

Mount Blanca, 14,317 feet high, in the Sangre de Cristo Range near Alamosa.

either end, and performed a minor operation. He got up, swinging his new hardware and never knew the difference."

Carpenter is among the last of the pioneers. The times he spanned are gone and yet they are everywhere in the mountains and beyond, in faces, lives, and places. Men like Hilkey and Carpenter have given shape and character to the state. They have also given it a flavor that is as much a legend and a longing as anything. In the men, as well as in the places, are the roots of what everyone wants the West to be, an honest fiction which makes reality bearable.

Durango is an extension of that honest fiction, a hearty town not far from where Utah, Colorado, Arizona, and New Mexico come together. Once a bawdy supply point and smelter for the Silverton mines, Durango now draws about seventy thousand visitors a year to its narrow-gauge railroad and about a third of that to its melodrama, held in a superbly restored Victorian hotel, the Strater. Although all of its false-fronted stores are gone and the town is busy and prosperous, the aura is unmistakably western. Utes from nearby Ignacio and Towaoc and Navajos from Arizona and New Mexico mingle with the crowds along Main Street where a two-block-long "instant West" has been erected by the Denver and Rio Grande Western Railroad. Local men in big Stetsons, cowboy boots, and bolo ties fastened with chunk turquoise cheerily tend to business, Denver-style. Some of them, like Earl Barker, Jr., who runs the Strater, are aggressive and strongly civic-minded, and determined to keep Durango one of the liveliest towns on the western slope. Tourism, naturally, is big business. "They want to sop up that damned atmosphere," remarked one Durango man. "It's gotten to be a real disease. If the railroad weren't the last of its kind, you couldn't pay people to make that dirty trip."

In summer, as early as four in the morning, railroad buffs begin to clog the little orange depot, shivering in the predawn which will soon change to

Summer thunderstorm over South Park.

a hot and dusty day in Durango. The first train departs with a low and mournful whistle that still sends shivers up the backs of many who have lived in Durango all their lives. A cloud of soot erupts from the smokestack and as cameras click and children wave goodbye, the engineer blows the whistle again and number "four-seventy-waterbag" is on its way down the yard-wide track to Silverton. For the next forty miles the train rocks along the Animas River, through a deep gorge and lush farmland, all the while belching black and white smoke, coughing around the curves, and sighing as she slows down.

At night, when the tourists have gone and the Durango depot is dark, the tired engine sits alone on the track, still sighing and coughing, very gently, as little clouds of steam rise from her flanks. This is the time the railroad men say is their time, when they go around from engine to engine, turning valves, stoking fires, keeping the iron horses alive. They are not much on

Diamond Belle Saloon, Strater Hotel, Durango.

Narrow-gauge railroad yard, Durango.

sentiment but they will tell you how everything works, proudly, as if they were showing off a new grandchild or a prize-winning lot of tomatoes.

The passenger trains were once the undisputed king of Colorado transportation. Now the king is an impoverished prince, aged and waiting to die. Only the California Zephyr remains and its future looks grim. The last passenger train to begin and end its run in Colorado was abandoned in 1968 and with it went an era.

Along the route from Denver to Craig they still call it the Yampa Valley Mail although the tiny two-car train didn't carry mail for the last decade of its existence. The railroad bed it followed every day was the old "Moffat Road," built by David Moffat, a stodgy, acquisitive man who sank his entire gold-mining fortune into the railroad that was to run from Denver to Salt Lake City. The railroad got as far as Craig, 232 miles from Denver but less than halfway from Salt Lake.

In its last years, the Yampa Valley Mail carried no food, no drinks, and few passengers, and its conductors were old men. Yet at every stop—Toponas, Bond, Kremmling, Tabernash, Fraser, State Bridge and the rest—the people came shyly, straight-faced, and proud. They came to put relatives off and on and to trust small children to conductors. Simple, warm, and slow, these men always spoke of the fact that they served on Moffat's Denver and Salt Lake Railway before it was bought by the Denver and Rio Grande Western in 1948. One, a great barrel-chested man with red cheeks said, "I'm a Moffat man. Only the engineer and trainman are Rye-o Grande." He looked out of the window as the train entered the 6.9-mile-long Moffat Tunnel, the first of fifty tunnels between there and Craig. "Know how they laid this railroad out?" he asked solemnly. "They went down to Texas and got 'em a big rattlesnake and turned it loose." As a load of skiers got off at Winter Park, a passenger asked, "Is the train always this full?" The old conductor shook his head. "Only when we have these flatboard idiots," he said.

Far away from trains and things, a solitary figure paused at the top of an 11,000-foot peak just as the morning sun struck the snowy tips of the ponderosa. Two feet of snow had fallen since the night before and it hung like cotton from the trees and blew in little, noiseless clouds as the air began to stir. Away and away the peaks stood out, row after row fading on and on into the distance, blue, cold, and oddly ephemeral, as if the earth had just been born and was clean again. The man paused only a moment to look at it because the lure of the uncut slope was too strong and he was too good a skier not to know what he could do with it. The deep powder was like going through a cloud and his skis seemed to float him down the slope, very

Skiing under the crest; Crested Butte Mountain.

fast, with the snow blowing up to his face and the natural exhilaration making it all but impossible to remember there was an end to the run. He came to it soon enough and looked back at the curve he'd made, perfect and clean in the snow.

"Skiing is a narcissistic sport," he said later. "It's the only sport where you can look back and see what you've done." He'd broken the slope that morning alone, before the crowds and the other patrolmen. There was a frustration, he said, "of not wanting to disturb what nature has done to the slope and the challenge of the thing itself. If you ski it well, you'll put a regular pattern in it that will heighten nature. If you don't do it well, you've taken a liberty with nature."

At night he was the last one down, alone on the mountain with the sun already set and the bitter cold stinging his cheeks. "I love it," he said. "It's the only time I get the feeling it's all mine."

Most skiers are as proprietary about their slopes as they are dedicated to the sport which, as an ex-Air Force officer explained, "is the closest thing to total freedom you can find except flying." They will endure ripping winds and sub-freezing temperatures, they will travel all night and get up at dawn, they will go after new slopes with the same enthusiasm a mountain climber has for untried peaks, and they will grumble about the danger of skiing becoming a contact sport. "Nowadays," said a man who taught skiing at

Skiing at Mid-Vail.

Camp Hale near Leadville during World War Two, "I either get a Cat to dump me out on top of some mountain and strap on my crosscountry skis or else I take my snowshoes and a sleeping bag and disappear for three days."

Along with the pure, invigorating, and unpretentious sport of skiing have come various embellishments. Mood music is carried by loudspeaker down many slopes. Drinks are served at 10,000 feet. Mink parkas and lamé stretch pants are offered in shops. And while most of the state's thirty-six ski areas have been cautious about devastating the landscape on the slopes, many builders of lift-level villages have not. One skier, noting the tight spread of expensive lodges, condominiums, and shops at Vail said, "It looks as if the mountain tilted and everything landed in a heap." But most of all, skiing has become something of a status symbol. A well-to-do Vail man who calls himself "just a ski nut" said, "Life at the top bears no resemblance to life at the bottom. The atmosphere of rich-rich down here is not rich-rich up there. I ski here because I know how good the mountain is, not because I want people to know I'm a millionaire."

Vail and Aspen, while the most social conscious, are also the best places to ski. No other resorts have more slopes, runs, trails, and variety of skiing. At Snowmass, Aspen's fourth ski area, is what its developers call "the ultimate mountain." Not only do they refer to the skiing but to the complex of villages below, built almost overnight with the help of a couple of computers called the Program Evaluation and Review Technique and the Critical Path Method. The population at Snowmass, as at Vail, is unusually well-heeled. A real-estate salesman for a Snowmass condominium said, "Vail has Senator Percy and the Murchisons and all those Texans but we have McNamara, one Guggenheim, and six board chairmen." Aspen and Vail, popular, prestigious, and with almost guaranteed skiing, attract the expert skier as well as the I-hate-to-ski man who comes to be seen with names such as these. For most people, however, there is no uncut slope at daybreak, waiting to be skied. There are new friends and old and that is why so many of them come. As the Vail newspaper once wrote, "Whether you want to pass the time on Riva Ridge or over a mellow brew, solitude refuses to set in." And as a man at Snowmass remarked, "If you want, you can be by yourself as much as thirty minutes at a time."

Condominium at base of ski lift, Aspen.

Lunchtime at Mid-Vail, a cafeteria 10,200 feet up Vail Mountain.

Snowmass is eight miles from Aspen which still reigns as the ski capital of the state. Once the scene of frenetic silver mining, Aspen dozed for six decades after the silver panic of 1893 until Walter Paepcke realized its potential in 1945. Paepcke, board chairman of the Container Corporation of America, saw Aspen not in terms of more dollars for himself but with a humanitarian's vision saw it as an international center for art, music, and study, secluded and congenial. Almost singlehandedly and backed with millions, Paepcke started the Aspen Music Festival and the Aspen Institute for Humanistic Studies and gave new impetus to the local ski trade. In 1949 the Goethe Bicentennial, held at the Institute, saw Albert Schweitzer stroll in front of the Jerome Hotel and Jose Ortega y Gasset wandering among the low-slung buildings of Aspen Meadows. With Paepcke as its mastermind, Aspen grew into a brainy, cultured, and well-bred community, as interested in Sophocles as it was in schussing. Two renowed architects, Herbert Bayer and Fritz Benedict became residents and designed understated yet elegant buildings which became foils for block after block of fanciful Victorian architecture. Ingrid Bergman came and so did Reinhold Niebuhr, Allen Dulles, Adlai Stevenson, Walter Reuther, and Eero Saarinen who designed a supertent which houses the Music Associates of Aspen and the International Design Conference.

Paepcke died in 1960, leaving behind a town that is a whimsical blend of foreign accents, beards, bicycles, miniskirted college girls waiting tables, earnest young men discussing war and politics over beer and pizza, middle-age stability, formidable snobbery, and as passionate a devotion to skiing as to the arts. Homogenized, prosperous, and with an air of I-don't-have-to-prove-it-to-you, Aspen glows with life at the top at the same time it bends with a touch of humility. Little girls still sell lemonade in summer, mothers still push babies down the street, and lift operators still say good morning. This is a town where a doctor has a gold-painted bedpan hung outside his door, where Henry James' grandson runs a bookstore, where the radio station is called KSNO, and where inside the Red Onion an aging ski instructor blows smoke through his nostrils and says, "I've got to have it all the time—action you know."

Top of Snowmass at Aspen.

Skier or not, there comes a time when the good loneliness of the mountains becomes a panacea to a man who has been too close to his fellow creatures. He finds it in wilderness and along the dinosaur back of the Continental Divide or anywhere not yet contaminated by civilization. "Back in" is what some call it and "back in" is where they are reborn. "Back in" is where something happens. Perhaps it is the lack of oxygen or the deafening silence, the

Skiing on the shoulders of Crested Butte Mountain; Elk Mountains in background. (Overleaf)

Maroon Belles, near Aspen.

oneness with the place or the incomprehensible pale distance which finally grips a man and, with his eyes watering, makes him feel he could fly over it all like a white-tailed ptarmigan or water pipet. "Back in," at some time or another, a man may come as close as he'll ever get to unraveling the mystery. All the patterns of life and death and mutation are there in perfect order. Everything fits. And yet and yet . . .

Crestone group in the Sangre de Cristo Mountains, looking south from Hermit Pass, eighteen miles due west of Westcliffe. Peaks left to right are: Crestone, 14,294; Kit Carson, 14,165; Mount Adams, 13,931; unnamed, 13,120; unnamed, 13,544.

Canyons
and Mesas

I do not know much about gods; but I think that the river
Is a strong brown god — sullen, untamed and intractable. . . .

T. S. ELIOT

THE RIVER BEGINS INNOCENTLY ENOUGH, high on the Continental Divide, south of Rabbit Ears Pass. It swings north toward Steamboat Springs, worming its way out of the mountains which gave it birth. Fed by creeks named Walton, Mad, Fish, Soda, and Fortification, the Yampa becomes a respectable river by the time it cuts across the valley that bears its name between Steamboat and Craig. By then, the land has leveled off and the river that has fed it and made it rich begins to change. No longer friendly, the river arches its back and plunges into a corkscrew of rapids and curves that no man has gone through and lived to tell about. Brown, angry, and imperious, the river slashes through the canyons east of Dinosaur National Monument. Then it levels off again as it enters the monument boundary.

The road to Deer Lodge Park cuts off from the main road a few miles north of the sleepy little town of Elk Springs. It is a Park Service road, newly constructed, and it ends at the Yampa, near where Disappointment Creek and the Vale of Tears stand opposite one another. Along this road workmen discovered the grave of a settler's little girl and built the road around her, marking her place with four sticks and a pile of rocks.

Black Canyon of the Gunnison National Monument from the north
rim. Maximum depth is 2700 feet; tree at lower left is sixty feet high.

Chimney Rock, near Towaoc. (Overleaf)

All rafts put in at Deer Lodge Park for there the river has calmed down and barely moves along the sand bars and shoreline. Shortly, however, it penetrates the sharp façade of the canyon and follows it for the next forty-five miles until it joins the Green at Echo Park. In spring, the Yampa screams through the canyon, white-frothed, ripping at rocks and trees. In summer, the river seems exhausted and only Warm Springs rapids are big enough to worry about for several reasons. Some years ago heavy rains loosened the top of the draw above the springs and sent crashing into the river ton upon ton of small rocks which today make a bed about twenty feet high. At this same spot, a few years later, but across the river to the south, a hundred-foot sliver of sandstone dropped straight into the river, changing its course even more. As one looks up from the rapids at the pale pink place where the rock used to be, the other half appears to be clinging by a thread, an enormous arrow pointed directly at the helpless voyager.

The river, hushed, muddy, and powerful beneath its smooth face, does not provoke the same feeling as the sea. Its smell is one of mud, its texture is gritty, its color brown and when the sun strikes it, a dirty yellow. The

Horned toad, 3½ inches long; Mesa Verde National Park.

*Yampa River Canyon at Warm Springs campground, Dinosaur
National Monument. Leopard frog right foreground.*

river, though wildly beautiful, is no friend of man and the canyon even less so. The peace it bestows rather grudgingly gives way to exhilaration and then to a vague sadness. For this is not man's river and he is simply an intruder. All he can do is glide along in solitude, observing the citizens of the river—the golden eagle and the somber raven, the unconcerned mule deer and her young, the little shore beaver swimming along the banks and building no dams, the molting Canadian geese waddling through the shad scale, and the placid leopard frog sitting on the mud bank.

Other people a long time ago found the canyon an alien land and used one of its vast caves only for the storage of grain. They drew pictures of buffalo, deer, hunters, mountains, and lakes on the sandstone walls but they did not attempt to depict the canyon or the river or even a fish. Perhaps they, too, felt the indifference of the place even as they sought its protection and fished its waters. The sleek Colorado squawfish, the humpback sucker with a razor on its back, the bony Colorado chub, all these fed the aboriginals and swim today in diminished numbers.

Petroglyph, probably prehistoric Apache, Apishapa River Canyon, eastern Colorado.

Howard Munsell, cowboy and Indian relic authority, Fowler.

Penitente crosses at Sopris Plaza, five miles west of Trinidad, 1955.
Crosses were carried on Good Friday by Spanish-American men seek-
ing penance. This area will be flooded by the Trinidad Reservoir by
1975.

Beginning of canyon and mesa country west of Meeker.

At night, the little bats flit noiselessly beyond the fire, made Indian style, with only the tips of the logs burning. The cottonwoods swish at water's edge, the low forest of juniper and sage becomes fragrant in the coolness. Beyond the cliff towering a thousand feet or more, the eyes search the moonless sky for the North Star or some familiar thing. Then all at once comes a satellite, headed over Utah. Swiftly, it is gone and night covers the canyon and the river. Crickets, mosquitoes, a mouse after the dinner crumbs, and far away, the last cry of a stricken animal.

The Yampa River finishes its life at Echo Park near Steamboat Rock. There, a few miles east of the Utah border it joins the Green which is only a visitor to Colorado. Beginning in the Wind River Mountains of Wyoming, the Green curves through the western edge of Colorado, then turns southwest into Utah where it eventually empties into the Colorado River.

The Green, rather than the Yampa, has been the scene of life, death, and adventure ever since cycads, ginkgoes, and horsetails grew in what was then a swamp. A hundred and fifteen million years ago when the slush of the Jurassic period trapped the tiny hoplosuchus, the weird and weighty Apatosaurus, and all the lizard hips, bird hips, and other species of the times, it trapped them along the Green and hardened them into the Morrison formation. The monument's well-filled quarry lies south of Utah's Split Mountain. At Jones Hole Creek, barely over the Utah line, Indians came seven centuries before Christ and stayed for nearly two after. During the nineteenth century, General William Ashley, William Manley, and Major John Wesley Powell shot the Green's man-eating rapids but ignored the tamer Yampa. Also along the Green, on the Colorado side, came the mountain men to rendezvous at Brown's Hole near the awesome Canyon of the Lodore. Sprawled along the grassy banks, they exchanged beaver for whisky and powder and picked themselves squaws from the Ute bands which kept constant camp nearby. By the time the mountain men trapped the last of the beaver in the 1840s, Brown's Hole had become notorious for its collection of bank robbers, cattle thieves, and desperadoes who often aided the Brown's Hole

Rifle. Anvil Point's oil-shale deposits in background.

settlers in exchange for food and a hiding place. Butch Cassidy, one of the most successful bank robbers, horse thieves, and cattle rustlers of all time was once described by an aged Brown's Hole pioneer as doing "far more to redistribute the wealth in northwestern Colorado than Franklin Delano Roosevelt, and he did it a whole lot quicker, and without any red tape."

Today, Brown's Park as it is now called, is simply a lovely valley with a few isolated ranches and cabins nearby. Butch Cassidy's name is all but forgotten, except perhaps to an old park ranger who lives alone at the Echo Park campground. He has followed all of Cassidy's trails from Wyoming to Texas. From the dirt road above the Chew ranch, he looks out across the shadowed canyons and watches the wisps of sunlight playing across the mesas. It looks like an aerial view and he points to a distant rock and says, "There's where Butch laid over on his way to Robber's Roost."

At the south edge of the Vermilion Bluffs, not far from the monument boundary is Greystone, population two. A man and his wife live there, tending the small store, single gas pump, and post office. One year, Greystone had a one hundred per cent increase in population. A retired couple came in a trailer but could not stand the awful loneliness there on Vermilion Creek. In fall, California hunters drive their campers into Greystone and go off in search of deer. Once they arrived with a pilfered parking meter jutting out of a station wagon and implanted it in front of the one store on the one street in Colorado's tiniest town.

The people of the canyon country are fewer than anywhere else in the state. Their faces reflect the land which has infused them with grit and practicality. They move slowly, but are not lazy; their humor is raw; their lives uncomplicated and filled with simple pleasures. Most of them do not make much money but their places are neat, their kitchens comfortable, and their handshake warm once they have sized up a newcomer. Many of the younger men, newly arrived with degrees in geology and engineering, work in the oil fields at Rangely and speak of the places they left in Texas and Oklahoma. The older men in that area who did not go to college are noticeably proud of a handsome junior college atop a mesa overlooking the town. Television is ever-present in cafés, barbershops, and restaurants and when a Western comes on they all stop what they are doing and watch. They do not care much about news and the casualty report from Vietnam seems as incongruous as an announcement about air pollution. Their interest lies here at home where the ties of neighborliness run strong. It is particularly noticeable in spring when the ewes are lambing and men come from every ranch within a hundred miles to help one another. Sometimes weeks are involved, yet no money exchanges hands.

"If you laid a hundred-dollar bill in front of those boys, they wouldn't touch it," explained a sheepman. "One bad May a blizzard hit us on the divide right after we had lambed and shorn the ewes. The boys and I rode all night trying to keep the herd together. When morning come and it was cleared, there was a couple hundred lambs and ewes all froze to death. The boys didn't say nothing. They just piled 'em up and soaked 'em with kerosene and set 'em afire. Then they rode two days more driving the rest of the herd up the valley. Not one man felt he ought to get paid or needed a whole lot of thanks. They just done it, that's all."

The canyon men are outdoor men. They are experts with a gun and can take a hunter over an uncharted trail to get his buck. In winter, when the cold creeps up the canyon and the river becomes sluggish with half-formed ice, the canyon men button up and set off in the pale light of a laggard dawn. By foot, jeep, or horseback, and not always in search of game, these men have a driving necessity to stand off from civilization. In winter, as one man put it, "I got to feel the place." One scours the remote canyons for pictographs during the winter. Another looks for dinosaur bones. A sinewy Italian in his seventies simply pits his amazing strength against the elements and is fed by the fact that he is able to outwalk and outlast men half his age.

While the rugged country of northwestern Colorado breeds a taciturn and tough kind of individual, it can also destroy him. Deep in the canyons, across the sage-covered mesatops, along the scruffy arroyos and creek banks are the remains of lives that no one remembers. A crumbling sheepherder's wagon sits on a lonely flat, battered by winds that must have once penetrated and driven away the man who lived there. Along the Yampa is a tiny shack made of untrimmed logs and mud. The back wall is the side of a huge boulder. A crude bed is nailed to the timber, filled with rotting gunny sacks that once served as a hermit's bedclothes.

At a place called Skull Creek is the half-wrecked cabin of a man named Caisson. What sort of man was he, this Caisson, whose personal papers covering thirty years are strewn knee-deep in two rooms of his house and out the back door onto the splintered porch? A handful of dusty letters and documents reveals that he came from Fort Smith, Arkansas, before 1920 and established a general store and post office, naming the post office, which served himself and his wife, Caisson, after himself. He had a few cattle, stored snow in a water tank, loaned money, took a radio technician's course by mail in 1929, and invested in a gold mine at five cents per share. In the

Roy Stryker of Grand Junction, director of the Farm Security Administration photographic project during the 1930s.

Sheepherder's wagon, North Park near Walden. Park Range in background.

late forties, when everyone in that part of the country was hot on the trail of uranium, the old man bought himself a geiger counter. But he never made any money and, from the looks of his place, left suddenly. What does it mean, a man's life recorded in a pile of junk in a hard, dry land in the middle of nowhere? Somehow the loneliness comes through and the man's persistence as well as the realization that time has left a kind of monument in his behalf. And what finally happened to Mr. Caisson? A grocer says matter-of-factly that he died one day between his house and the road and was pretty well et up by buzzards.

If the canyon land can kill a man slowly with a half-crazed loneliness or swallow him suddenly in one of its precipices, it can also strike him down in another way. In spring and summer, flash floods whip out of the mesa country in an agony that shakes the land. The beginning is a blue-black cloud that sweeps slowly across the distant mesas, repeating their shape in

Howard Munsell's cabin and gate; Apishapa River country near Fowler.

Canyon and mesa country near Hotchkiss, not far from the Black Canyon of the Gunnison National Monument.

a long finger. Sometimes, as the storm descends to the mesa, a brilliant sun-lit cloud remains above, bathing the landscape in an eerie translucence. The dull limestone, the innocuous shale, the pastel sandstones, and the stubbly stuff of the desert, all of these become exquisite in the golden light of a sky giving birth to a storm. Far away, the rain starts. Lightning races to the horizon in half a dozen places at once. And then, slowly across the mesa-tops, gathering resonance from the canyons, comes the thunder, sounding like the empty stomach of a giant. The raindrops fall with a powerful splat. But they are in no hurry and out there on the mesatop there is no deluge at first, only the scattered drops that discolor the soil and send the smell of the plants and wet rock to the nostrils. A cottontail races around the side of a bush and disappears. A little whiptail lizard darts into a ledge hole. And then a crow glides low, casting the final shadow of the day.

Colorado National Monument.

Colorado River near Grand Junction.

The first thought is to get off the lightning-ridden mesa and escape to a sheltered place in the canyon itself. And so, coming off the mesa, along a road that becomes sticky and unsure with the increasing drops, one does not think of dangerous water below. The stream beds, passed an hour earlier, are still dry. Even the river that flows along the canyon floor is still nothing more than a trickle.

The dirt road that winds along the canyon floor has a little tongue of water running across it. Strange. Perhaps a spring that was not noticed before. And then all at once from the canyon above comes an ear-splitting roar as if an entire city is collapsing. After a terrifying scramble to higher ground, one looks down at the dry creek bed, fast disappearing as a wall of water fifteen feet high descends with a tangle of uprooted trees and rocks. The water laps up the creek bed, plunges over a precipice, and turns the baby river into a savage.

In the paper the next day is a story about an old cowboy and his horse who were down there when it hit. They found the man's body all right but gave up looking for his horse.

This particular canyon is neither beautiful nor inviting. What exists there exists by accident or pure stubbornness. Its color is truly black, its walls crusty. The only view is down, straight down into the depths of the Black Canyon of the Gunnison National Monument. Here, nature seems to have burst open the bowels of the earth to create a canyon that is narrow, treacherous, and spellbinding.

Visitors usually turn off U.S. 50 east of Montrose, drive the six miles to the monument, have a look, and drive straight out. One signed his name in the registry book: "Boris Karloff." In the middle of summer, a young woman emerged from a California car, ran to the rim, and said to her companion, "It turns me on." Just then, a small boy pitched a rock over the side and hung over the rail to watch it disappear along the two-thousand-foot drop. "Okay, Mom," he said solemnly. "Now let's go see Steve Canyon."

Late one afternoon, a shaft of sunlight emerged from the clouds and struck a solitary piñon growing from the top of a rock spire half as high as the canyon. The tenacity of life in the canyon was embodied in that tree, noble and straight that it was, reaching for the sunlight that penetrated the shadows only an hour or two each day. Meanwhile, a half dozen cattle bypassed a cattle guard and walked dully toward the precipice, stopping now and then to chew on the grass. No one seemed to care that they were about to kill

Black Canyon of the Gunnison National Monument from the south rim.

Augie Goveia, dam-construction worker, Morrow Point Dam, Cure-canti project, Gunnison River.

themselves. There was not a ranch within miles and the motorists merely honked to get them out of the way.

For all its frightening appearance from above, the canyon has a primeval beauty at its bottom by virtue of the river. Spewing over mossy boulders and jamming against the canyon walls, the Gunnison is a hard-to-get-to place where man can be by himself and sometimes see a bighorn sheep. Local fishermen who call themselves "the Gunnison navy" regularly take twenty-two-inch trout at Poison Springs Draw. Far above, at Chasm View overlook, a sign warns: "Don't throw rocks. Fishermen below." To which someone has added: "the fools."

Along its southwestern border, Colorado thrusts a bunch of chubby fingers toward New Mexico's blue haze. These are the great mesas of the state, high, lonesome, and lovely. From them it is possible to see the La Sal and Abajo Mountains looming out of Utah and the rosy desert spreading into Arizona. Shiprock, that ghostly mass of sandstone, rises pale and seemingly in full sail from the wasteland just inside New Mexico.

North rim, Mesa Verde National Park. Lowest bench is bed of oldest road to the top of Mesa Verde. In background is Hesperus Peak, 13,225 feet high, in the La Plata Mountains.

Of all the canyons and mesas in Colorado, none is more fabled nor compelling than Mesa Verde National Park. Nineteen miles from where it begins its nonchalant ascent from the Montezuma Valley, this complex of mesas ends hundreds of feet above the canyon floor. There, in deep, vast, and rugged canyons named Spruce Tree, Navajo, Fewkes, Cliff, and Soda are the remains of tenements built and deserted seven hundred years ago.

On a wintery day, when the tourists are not about and the late afternoon sun warms the stones that are marked by ancient feet, one senses the presence of those long-departed souls. Perhaps it is because of the utter silence of these cities crammed into caves. Or perhaps it is because the setting is so enormous and the signs of habitation nonexistent except in these neatly swept, half-ruined ruins. There is admiration for primitive architects who could design a perfect tower and put windows in the right places, for the masons whose mortared stones have withstood so much time and weather, and for the builders whose underground kivas are just a few inches short of being exact circles.

Looking up from where the National Park Service has erected an inconspicuous metal stairway, one sees footholds going up the bare rock. The barefoot squaws, carrying water jars, climbed here to collect water trapped in mesatop potholes. Their men clambered down with a deer slung across their backs. They must have been acrobats for archaeologists have yet to find skeletons with broken bones. They suffered from arthritis, however, and the park museum displays a pair of pre-Columbian crutches near a couple of grinning mummies named Esther and Jasper. (The Chief Park Ranger was hailed one day in the museum by an elderly woman who had been contemplating the remains of Esther. "Tell me, young man," she demanded, "how did you know her name was Esther?")

There are five thousand ruins in the eighty-square-mile park, of which less than fifty have been excavated and only two hundred identified. Most of these are on the mesatop where the Indians lived for twelve centuries before moving into the natural caves in the cliffs shortly after A.D. 1200. By the beginning of the fourteenth century, the sprawling tenements of Mesa Verde were deserted, their citizens driven off by a thirty-year drought which devastated those peaceful farmers. Archaeologists believe that the remainder of the tribe drifted south along the Rio Grande and joined the pueblo people whose lives were so similar to their own.

Though beaver trappers and miners saw the cliff dwellings in the nineteenth century, their minds were on far greater things and they left the ruins undisturbed. In 1874, government photographer William Henry Jackson dragged

Spruce Tree House, Mesa Verde National Park. Beneath the stone floor are three circular ceremonial rooms called kivas.

[179]

his enormous view camera up the mesa and shot Two-Story House on an eighteen- by twenty-four-inch glass negative which he developed in a nearby tent. Fourteen years later, two cowboys named Richard Wetherill and Charlie Mason were riding along Sun Point in search of stray cattle when they found Cliff Palace perched in a cave high on the opposite wall. Wetherill and his four brothers also discovered the now-excavated Spruce Tree House, Square Tower, Step House, Long House and Mug House ruins plus others which have not yet been touched. They left their signatures on the walls and carted off pottery and baskets that had not been buried by centuries of falling sandstone. In the late eighteen hundreds, citizens of Mancos and Durango rated artifact hunting among their favorite pastimes. Fine old pots appeared on dining room tables and youngsters displayed flat-headed skulls along with their rattlesnake skins.

Gustaf Nordenskjold, a wealthy Swedish baron, began a legitimate larceny of the ruins in 1891 and amassed the cream of Mesa Verde artifacts at the Durango depot. Jim Jarvis, a member of one of the town's leading families, got out a restraining order which was heard all the way to Washington. After some debate, the baron's load was waved down the little track of the narrow gauge and ultimately landed in Helsinki.

Eighty visitors puffed up the trail to Mesa Verde in 1908, two years after it was made a national park. When the first park road was opened in 1913, motorists steamed up the west side of Point Lookout, a bathtub-shaped butte rising two thousand feet straight up. Chugging through a sea of mud and boulders, the cars usually backed up to keep the gas flowing from the tank to the engine. The one-way traffic was regulated by a Mancos operator who received calls from telephones located at the top and bottom of the giddy road. A popular sport was negotiating the road without phoning. Tourists who happened to get to the top could rent rooms for fifty cents and get a somewhat primitive meal for a quarter.

Today, a half-million visitors per year drive up the new but still formidable road to Mesa Verde, assuaged by prospects of a deluxe campground or bedding down in a carpeted, air-conditioned cabin with a hundred-mile view. They swarm over the ruins, cameras clicking, and listen to the ranger-archaeologists talk about everything from Indian burial habits to the content of ancient fecal matter. During one busy day in summer, when he was giving a lecture to a busload of naturalists, a seasonal ranger noticed that a middle-aged lady had dropped off a ledge to some underbrush twenty feet below. Seeing that she was unhurt, he continued his talk, shouting half of it down to the woman who hadn't wanted to interrupt him long enough to get hoisted back up.

Cliff Palace, Mesa Verde National Park, architecturally the finest and largest ruin in the park. (Overleaf)

Jack Wade, Chief Park Ranger, Mesa Verde National Park; now retired.

The ruins are sometimes occupied by others than tourists and archaeologists. A mischievous young boy whose father worked in the park used to dress up like an Indian and sneak off before dawn to one of the kivas in Spruce Tree House. He would build a fire and when the first load of tourists arrived, climb out of the kiva with a war whoop. Once, a group of Mesa Verde girls formed what they called "The Kiva Bridge Club," which met underground every week, and had lapel pins made bearing that legend. Another time, a teen-ager decided that Mesa Verde ought to have a swimming pool and turned on the valve of an empty water-storage tank. Believing it would take days to fill, he went home. That night, driving up the mesa, he noticed a stream of water coming across the stunted forest and tore up to his overflowing "swimming pool."

"What you notice about him first and what stays with you the longest is his face. You feel good just looking at him." This is the way another ranger describes Jack Wade, former Chief Park Ranger at Mesa Verde. A trader who has known him a long time says he is "all sunburned with living." He has the look of a man who has laughed often and much. Yet behind the mirth in his eyes and the upward curl of his mouth is the fermentation of a life spent in nature's raw domain. He knows all about Indians and wild ani-

Shiprock, ghostly volcanic plug in New Mexico, forty miles distant.

mals and weather and bad places and how a man takes care of himself. He is taciturn yet by saying little he conveys the leanness of the life he's led, the kind of life that one finds in diminishing numbers on the mesas these days.

His father was a trader to the Indians and his mother died when he was young. So when his father married a woman that "even the good Lord Himself couldn't get along with," young Wade struck out alone for his Uncle John Wetherill's dude ranch in Kayenta, Arizona. John was one of the brothers who discovered the Mesa Verde ruins and was married to Wade's aunt. The boy learned to break and wrangle horses as well as how to guide people over the wild Navajo country. Navajo became his second language and the people became his own. Their canyons and deserts grew to be as familiar to him as his own patch of land near Mancos. The land taught him all he knew. Once he hauled a five-hundred-pound dedication plaque all by himself across the wilderness from Kayenta to Rainbow Bridge. It took five long days to get there, dragging the plaque on a travois behind his horse, over scorching desert and rough sandstone. For years he guided Eastern dudes all the way to Mexico and back and numbered among his customers Zane Grey who, having brought his own cook, insisted on having a separate camp "where he'd just get off by himself and not talk to anybody." One two-thousand-mile pack trip went from Altar, Mexico, through the White Mountains, Flagstaff, the

Hopi country, the Grand Canyon, and ended at Kayenta four months later with four saddle-sore New Yorkers and their thirty-three pack horses. Another time, a wealthy New Yorker hired him to dig up a dinosaur track, if he could find one. Wade knew the Navajo country and where in its vastness the dinosaurs had roamed. A week later he toted the cumbersome package to the post office.

Eventually he drifted back to Mesa Verde which he had first seen as a child. By that time it was the Depression and he was lucky to land a job as a packer-guide to the horse concessioner. He learned the canyons and mesas as he had once learned the desert and became immersed in the relationship of man to nature. Caught by the land spiritually, he became part of it physically as he lived for weeks at a time along its jagged rims and treacherous depths. When he finally became a park ranger, he already knew every draw, every unmapped ruin, every game trail. He was dispatched to fire patrol on ten-day jaunts that took him even deeper into the wilderness. For two years he rode such missions, coming in only to wash, shave, and get a good night's sleep. Later he established a series of fire stations and drew detailed charts which enabled rangers to reach the scene of a blaze within hours.

Once when Park Service superiors felt that the porcupines were killing too many trees and ought to be controlled, Wade countered that through migration porcupines pretty well controlled themselves. This time an emphatic message came from Washington: *porcupines do not migrate. They are aimless wanderers.* Wade was instrumental in beginning a long-term experiment which he says "was maybe the first time anybody researched a porcupine." First he captured the animals while patrolling on snowshoes in winter, deftly grabbing them on the underside of their tails where the quills do not grow. Next he forced them into a wire cone and put metal tags on their ears. For weeks he trapped hundreds of porcupines. Then he sat back and watched where they went. He learned that they traveled over definite routes and came out five or ten miles from where he first caught them. For three years he also found that only one out of five porcupines was a baby. Then came a year when not a single baby porcupine was among all of Wade's subjects at Mesa Verde. Puzzled, he and his rangers bored five thousand trees and discovered that porcupines ran in twenty-year cycles. At the end of every twenty-year period he found evidence that either porcupines ceased to reproduce or through disease they began to die off. Then they slowly increased again to a new twenty-year height. Thus, reported Wade, porcupines are no menace except during their peak years when perhaps they should be controlled. The government reluctantly agreed.

Step House, Wetherill Mesa, Mesa Verde National Park. A ruin remarkable for having pit houses discovered under the rubble of the floor of the cave dwelling.

Today Jack Wade the outdoor man and embodiment of Mesa Verde lives nearly three hundred miles from his beloved country. His home is at Clarkdale, Arizona, not far from the old mining town of Jerome. Every now and then he comes back, not for old times' sake but because the land is an undeniable part of him. That, he says, is what no one understands anymore. The way the land grabs hold. The way it stays with you until the end.

A couple of canyons away from Jack Wade's old office is Wetherill Mesa, the newest of all the excavated ruins. For five years, archaeologists from the National Park Service and the National Geographic Society carted away tons of debris, discovered new mesatop ruins, stabilized three prime cliff dwellings and gathered reams of new scientific data.

After they had finished and gone away, Wetherill was almost the way the cliff dwellers had left it. True, the buildings were not intact, and the scientists had built stairways and left their mark in discreet and orderly fashion throughout but the feeling of being was still there. On a bluff overlooking Long House the wind rustled the piñon and the sun played across the courtyards of a tenement that seemed to be waiting for its owners. A ludicrous and yet fitting notion, that of expecting a brown and catlike native to spring from a crumbling room. One even strains his ears to hear something.

At Step House, three deer grazed a few yards from the ruins, nibbling without concern among the scrub oak. A tiny short-horned lizard basked on a rock and tried to hide his face with his front feet. In the soft, dusty earth beside the ruin were seven-hundred-year-old corn cobs and pottery shards, all a ribbed gray or with a trace of black paint made from the beeweed plant, which no longer grows at Mesa Verde. Scrawled in charcoal on the protected face of the cliff is the signature: "Wetherill 1891." Not far from it is a picture of a rectangular antelope that an artistic Indian incised into the rock so many centuries ago.

The Indians will never come back to Mesa Verde and those that live only a few miles away are no kin. The Utes are the last remaining tribe in Colorado and the only ethnic group living in the canyons and mesas of the state. Although they exert little influence over the state and are largely ignored by it, they nonetheless are significant because of their history and because of the fact that they have the biggest aggregate wealth of any organized group in the state.

Ute Mountain Ute boy, typical of the spirit of this branch of Utes.

Harriet Whyte of the Ute Mountain Utes with two of her grandchildren.

There are two separate tribes of Utes. One, the Ute Mountain Utes, has its headquarters at Towaoc, a dusty, modern village at the foot of Sleeping Ute Mountain. The other, the Southern Utes, is scattered along a checkerboarded reservation south of Durango, with headquarters at Ignacio, a non-Indian owned town. The attitudes and differences of the two tribes are directly attributed to their geography which, in turn, is linked to a fateful visit paid by Senator Harry Dawes of Massachusetts to the Cherokee nation of Oklahoma in 1887. At that time the Cherokees were living peacefully and profitably on their reservation, as were the Utes of Colorado. Dawes' words were to affect them all. He wrote that "there was not a family in that nation which did not own a home of its own. There was not a pauper in that nation, and the nation did not owe a dollar. Yet the defect of the system was apparent. They have got as far as they can go because they own their land in common. . . . There is no selfishness, which is at the bottom of civilization. Till this people will consent to give up their lands, and divide them among their citizens so that each can own the land he cultivates, they will not make much more progress."

At that time three bands of Utes lived on a large reservation along a strip in southern Colorado. The Weminuche band refused the individual allotment of 160 acres as passed under the senator's "General Allotment Act" and were moved to the desolate land south of Sleeping Ute Mountain, a few miles from their present site. Their land represents a block of more than a half-million acres. The Mouaches and the Capotes accepted allotments and spread out along the Pine River Valley. After that, what was left of their former reservation was bought by the government for $1.25 an acre and thrown open for settlement. Today, the best land along the roads that run through Southern Ute territory is owned by non-Indians. They have prosperous farms, fat herds of cattle, water rights, and populate the towns of Ignacio, Arboles, Juanita, Trujillo, and Tiffany which appear on most maps as part of the Southern Ute reservation. Southern Ute property is stretched out like a patchwork quilt, comprising in all about 305,000 acres.

The Southern Utes continued to farm, while those living at the mountain declined to become agrarians and were sustained through hunting and occasional food from the government. For nearly sixty years the Ute Mountain Utes lived in dire poverty and were seen in winter clothed in rags and walking barefoot to their decrepit hogans and tents. The fortune which fell on both tribes in the fifties was a mixed blessing. A total of $52,000,000 was suddenly in their hands and they did not know what to make of it.

Part of the money came from a land claim against the United States government for all the millions of acres taken from them in the last century. Part of it was from uranium, oil, and natural gas which were discovered in rapid succession on the wasteland to which they had been exiled. No one quite knows where all of the money went. Chunks of it went back to the government to reimburse them for buildings constructed at the Indian agency for government use. Some of it went into roads and improvements such as the medical building and recreation hall at Towaoc. The hall is complete with Olympic swimming pool, gymnasium, showers, and weight-lifting room, but the exuberant Utes forgot the air conditioning and on some days in summer the temperature soars past a hundred degrees indoors.

Two hundred dollars is now parceled out every other month to each man, woman, and child. The child's portion goes into trust at a Denver bank and is withdrawn at the age of eighteen. It amounts to about $6000 and is quickly spent on one or more automobiles, an item which is as much a part of a Ute's necessity as the horse was to his ancestors. Under a family plan, overseen by the federal government, the Utes can also withdraw a lump sum of $3000 to use for building a house, making improvements on it, or buying furniture. Often the furniture is left outside in the rain or is sliced up by the children. Government overseers worry more about such neglect than the unconcerned Utes for whom upkeep is neither necessary nor understood. Their houses are attractive though somewhat untidy frame buildings equipped with the latest gadgets, including toilets. Because they do not completely trust such conveniences, nearly every Ute has also constructed an outhouse in his backyard.

While the spending of the two tribes follows almost the same pattern, the leadership does not. The Southern Utes, because of their split-up reservation, are not clannish and have become nearly assimilated into the Anglo culture. Their government is in the form of a council which one man describes as "a lot of loose spokes."

There is also a council at Towaoc but it is superseded by a crusty old chief named Jack House. All of his people live where he can see them, except a few families scattered along the Mancos River Canyon. He has kept his tribe together, overriding bitterness and quarrels with his own inflexible personality. At most, his leadership has given his tribe a strong identity and tremendous loyalty as well as a carefree abandonment which sets them apart from the introspective Southern Utes. He is also a voice for his people which answers the government in no uncertain terms. Once, the Park Service asked him if it could use some gravel which the Mancos River had deposited millions of years ago on what is now Ute reservation. House reportedly replied that when the Mancos River rose again and deposited gravel on their side they could have it.

Recreation hall, Towaoc.

Eddie Box, Southern Ute.

The faces of the Utes at Towaoc are mostly gentle. A few are inscrutable. They are not, as outsiders think, lazy and spoiled by money. The tribe owns a large herd of cattle, which summers at the Ute ranch near Gunnison. A number of men work there while others have herds of their own. Some work at Cortez and a few are employed by the government at the Consolidated Ute Agency at Ignacio. Many of the youngsters drop out of high school but most finish and a few go on to college. One young man, just out of high school, announced happily that he was going to enlist in the Army and go to Vietnam "to see what it's like." A young girl works as a medical secretary at the clinic while her husband is a heavy-equipment operator for the Bureau of Indian Affairs. Harriet Whyte, the third woman to serve on the tribal council, has raised a large family and is embarking on another. She has adopted a three-year-old girl "because her mother didn't want her and I did" and has named her Tina White Skunk.

The Southern Utes, harder to find and even harder to talk to, seem to carry a burden that the Ute Mountain Utes do not have. One of them, Eddie Box, accuses them of having turned their backs on their Indian heritage. Box, in his forties, operates a small curio shop but supports himself by selling asbestos roof covering for a refining company. A worried, somber individual, Box wears his hair in braids because "it keeps reminding me of my Indian self and reminds the others of what they have got to do."

Basically, Box feels that his tribesmen must go back and find their roots, know who they are, and where they are going. They must no longer be ashamed of being Indian. They must relearn the old ways and find new courage within the old Indian religion. "Our religion," he explains, "is based on the spirit, on what a man finds inside himself." Yet religion and finding themselves again seems far from the thoughts of most Southern Utes. Box, however, keeps urging them to attend the deeply religious three-day Sun Dance

Eighteen-year-old Ute Mountain Ute with Camaro purchased with his coming-of-age money.

Edward and Jeanette Eyetooth, a couple from the Ute Mountain Ute tribe who live in the Mancos Canyon south of Mesa Verde.

which is held at Towaoc, Ignacio, and several other southwestern reservations, but only once a year. During these dances, says Box, an Indian must give himself up to spiritual things. He must forget his bi-monthly government check. The money, Box believes, has very nearly corrupted his people. "If we lose the money, we can go on," he says. "If we lose the spiritual side we cannot go on."

But Box is called a dreamer and a dissenter and a religious fanatic.

"There is nothing Box or the Utes can do," says a man with the Bureau of Indian Affairs. "It's not the policy of the government to encourage the Indian to drop his ways or to teach the old ones back to him either. He's a man in two cultures and a lot of things are going to be imposed on him. It's a changing world that's all."

Around Ignacio, "Indian" is almost a dirty word. The feeling seems to be that the sooner the Southern Utes forget their Indianness, the better life will be for everyone. No one praises them. No one is eager to hire them if there is another choice. A white shopkeeper in Ignacio said, "There's no Indian culture left here. We killed their pride."

A pretty Southern Ute high school girl said rather wistfully, "They want us to act like Anglos and when we do they say, 'Are you ashamed of being Indian?'" She put her hand to her heart. "Here is where we're Indian. It doesn't matter if we don't let them see it."

"Tradition is the enemy of progress," says a sign erected by the Presbyterians in Navajo country. To most men's way of thinking, it applies to the Utes as well. Jack House and Eddie Box are determined, in different ways, that tradition shall not perish. The old chief, defiant, proud, and intractable, has very nearly lived up to his Indian name of Hand That Stops the Sun. His people did not ask for the money nor has it really diminished the roots that are in their being and are reflected in their eyes. The young people do not stop very often to sit on a rock and look out at the desert, pale and indistinct and endless. Their new, fast cars take them to the reaches of experience and symbolize a pride and a freedom common to their ancestry. It is the old ones who understand what nature has given them and what tradition demands that they shall preserve. Once, a couple from New York stopped to photograph an old Ute sitting in the sun. The Indian said he'd been to New York, too, at Madison Square Garden with Pawnee Bill. The tourists asked how he'd liked New York and the Indian said he hadn't. Too many people? they asked. The old Indian looked up and shook his head. No sky, he said.

Index

Index

(Pages in italic indicate photographs.)

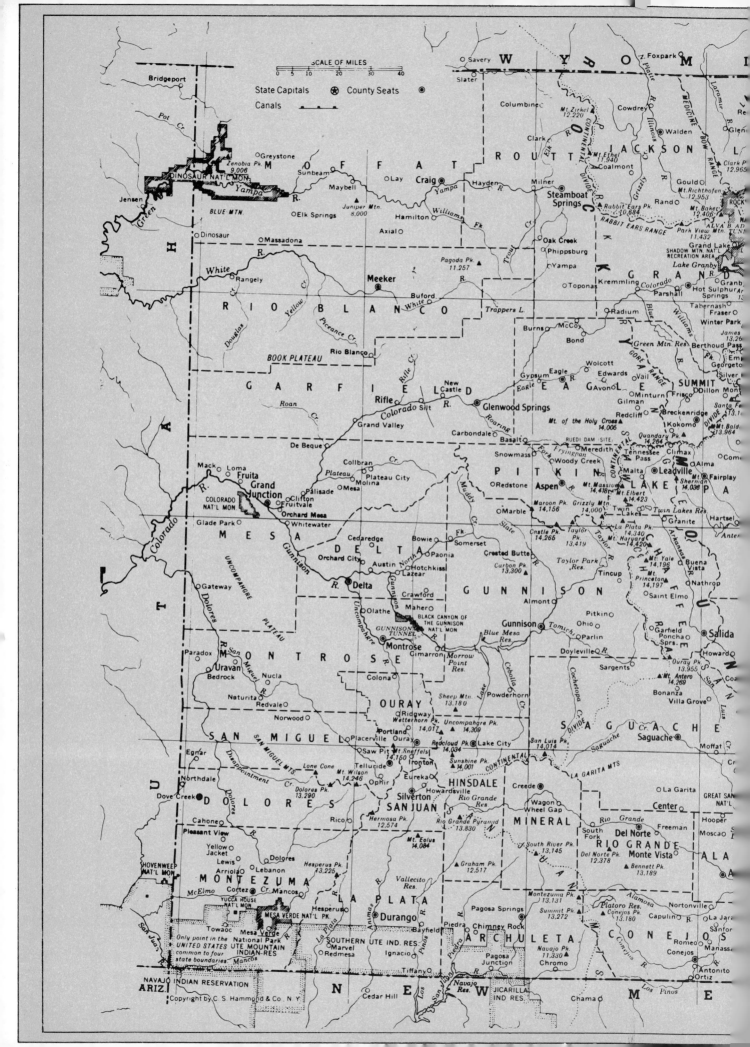

THE HOUSE OF
WOODEN SANTAS

Text Copyright © 1997 Kevin Major
Wood Carvings Design Copyright © 1997 Imelda George
Photography Copyright © 1997 Ned Pratt

All rights reserved. No part of this book may be reproduced by
any means, electronic or mechanical, including photography,
recording, or any information storage or retrieval system,
without permission in writing from the publisher.

Northern Lights Books for Children are published by
Red Deer College Press
Box 5005 56 Avenue & 32 Street
Red Deer Alberta Canada T4N 5H5

Acknowledgments
Edited for the Press by Peter Carver.
Design by Blair Kerrigan/Glyphics.
Printed and bound in Hong Kong for Red Deer College Press.

5 4 3 2 1

Financial support provided by the Alberta Foundation for the
Arts, a beneficiary of the Lottery Fund of the Government of
Alberta, and by the Canada Council, the Department of
Canadian Heritage and Red Deer College.

COMMITTED TO THE DEVELOPMENT OF CULTURE AND THE ARTS

THE CANADA COUNCIL | LE CONSEIL DES ARTS
FOR THE ARTS | DU CANADA
SINCE 1957 | DEPUIS 1957

Canadian Cataloguing in Publication Data

Major, Kevin, 1949–
The house of wooden Santas

(Northern lights books for children)
ISBN 0-88995-166-7

1. Christmas—Juvenile fiction. I. George, Imelda, 1964–
II. Pratt, Ned, 1964– III. Title. IV. Series.
PS8576.A523H68   1997   jC813'.54   C97-910530-7
PZ7.M2814Ho   1997

THE HOUSE OF
WOODEN SANTAS

STORY BY KEVIN MAJOR
WOOD CARVINGS BY IMELDA GEORGE

PHOTOGRAPHY BY NED PRATT

RED DEER COLLEGE PRESS

For Duncan

There was just Jesse and his mother.

But Jesse's mother had lost her job. She searched for months without finding another, and so she decided they should move out of the city to some place where it wasn't so expensive to live.

"No way," Jesse had said to her.

But her mind was made up. She sold off a pile of furniture and toys, and all the hockey equipment Jesse had outgrown. She packed up the old car and drove three hours on the highway, and down a side road another hour, until they reached the house she had read about in the ad.

The landlady, Mrs. Wentzell, met them at the front gate. She was a silver-haired woman with earrings that dangled like crazy, and a terrier in her arms that never stopped yapping.

"It's my daughter's house really," Mrs. Wentzell said. "They had to move away."

Jesse's mother was looking at the ocean beyond the house. "So beautiful," she sighed.

Jesse grunted. "Yeah. Right. Big deal."

Mrs. Wentzell's eyes narrowed in on Jesse. "My granddaughter is about your age. She loved it here."

When Mrs. Wentzell wasn't looking, Jesse sneered at the dog. The dog bared its pointed little teeth and growled.

"Ivan!"

Mrs. Wentzell clamped the jaws of the dog shut with her hand.

"Ivan the Terrier," muttered Jesse to himself. "Mighta known."

"I'm starting a business," his mother explained to Mrs. Wentzell. "Years ago I took up wood carving as a hobby . . . making figures, angels mostly. Now I've decided to try it full time. I've made a deal with a craft shop to carry my carvings." She paused. "I'll have the rent money to you as soon as they start to sell."

Mrs. Wentzell hesitated. "I don't know what my husband would have said. . . . "

"It'll work out. I'm sure of it."

Mrs. Wentzell finally nodded.

Jesse's mother started down the lane toward the house, a smile lighting her face.

Jesse followed glumly behind, down the lane to the front door.

TWENTY-FOUR DAYS TO CHRISTMAS

This Friday, the first day of December, Jesse burst through the same front door, home from school. He headed straight for the television, plunked himself down in front of it, set to play video games and watch cartoons.

His mother came marching out from the workroom, where she had been all day. A tough look of determination was set into her face.

She flicked off the TV and stood in front of it, her arms folded like an iron guard from one of the games he was about to play. "It's wonderful outside," his mother declared. "The fresh air will do you good."

Jesse erupted with a chorus of complaints. "It's boring here. They don't even have a hockey league. There's no shopping mall. There's not even a place to buy a hamburger!"

"Surely there are other things you could do," his mother insisted. "Christmas is coming. Santa is on his way. You *could* be getting ready for him."

"He probably won't even find this place . . . if there is a Santa, which I doubt!"

"Oh, Jesse."

Jesse pressed his lips together and stalked off.

He left his mother standing there, her arms still folded. She walked slowly back to her workroom.

Jesse banged his bedroom door shut.

Late that night, when his eyes were too heavy to open, he heard his mother creep into his room. She placed something on his bedside table and whispered close to his ear.

"In the House of Wooden Santas there's someone to keep you safe and take away your doubts. *Guardian Santa* protects you from the worries of the world." She planted a kiss on his cheek.

During the night Jesse stirred in his bed. Noise from another part of the house touched his sleep. His eyes drifted open for a few moments, just long enough for a vision of Santa Claus to fly into his dreams.

TWENTY-THREE DAYS
TO CHRISTMAS

J esse woke with a start, his head filled with Santa hovering in the air above him.

He blinked. He sat up quickly in bed. He looked up and down and around his room, and especially long at his bedside table. His room was just the same.

And he was sure his Saturday morning would be just the same. Bor-r-r-ring.

He fell back on the bed and thought of how he used to be up at seven, into his hockey gear, and at the apartment door, waiting for his mother to drive him to the arena. He could still hear the cheering crowd when he scored the winning goal in the second game of the play-offs. He looked over at the gold medal that hung off the corner of his dresser mirror.

Jesse crawled out of bed and made his way toward the living room, ready to curl up on the sofa in front of the TV. When he entered the room he came to a sudden stop. It was as if he had stepped into another world. He rubbed the sleep out of his eyes.

The room was filled with Christmas! Garlands of evergreens laced with silver stars and colored paper ribbon swirled up and over the windows and doors. On the walls hung wreaths wound red with dogberries, trimmed with dried flowers and herbs, cinnamon sticks and pine cones flecked with gold. Crepe paper chains streamed from the ceiling, heaps of nuts crowded the mantelpiece, and about it all drifted the smell of the woods and the crackling sound of fire in the fireplace.

The room had been cleared of all its furniture, except the old sofa and end tables. Not another thing remained. Including his video games. Including the TV.

"Mom!"

His mother emerged from her workroom, smelling still of evergreens, wood chips clinging to the wool of her sweater. In her hands she held a box. She laid it between them on the sofa.

Jesse looked at her, a squirming look, full of questions.

"Well," she said, "what do you think?"

"You did all this? Last night? After I went to bed?"

"I'm determined this is going to be our best Christmas ever."

She set the lid of the box aside. Pushing back the crumpled newspaper, she smiled as if to greet a friend.

"Something new I've been working on."

From the box she lifted a wooden figure, turning it upright so Jesse could see. She placed it in his hands. His fingers ran over the painted wood for a moment, and then he looked at his mother. A bit of a smile slumped across his face. He laid the figure on the mantel above the fireplace.

When he sat back on the sofa, his mother said, "Into the House of Wooden Santas comes a fine old chap. Some call him St. Nick or Father Christmas or Kris Kringle. I call this guy *Santa from Long Ago*. 'Cause he's come through snow and rain, across vast deserts, and over the seven seas. . . ."

"Mom . . ." Jesse groaned.

His mother looked at him. Her eyebrows narrowed.

"I'm getting too old for this stuff! I'm nine," he protested.

"Nobody's too old for a little magic in their lives! Look at me."

Jesse rolled his eyes. There was a long silence. He folded his arms and sat staring at the fire. His mother stared at the fire, too, and hummed "Santa Claus is Coming to Town" and pretended not to care.

"I like that figure," Jesse said finally. "I thought you only carved angels."

"I'm branching out."

"Oh."

"I'm expanding."

"Good."

There was another long silence.

"Okay. So can I keep him?"

His mother didn't say anything.

"Can I?"

"For today," she said. "We need the money."

"Knew it."

"There'll be others . . . in other outfits."

"Yeah, right."

"There will. I promise. I've been as busy as an elf in that workroom."

He sank into the sofa. "Now can I watch TV?"

His mother sat stiffly. Finally she gave in, went to another room, and lugged the TV back.

From time to time that day, during the commercials mostly, Jesse glanced at the mantel to check out Santa. The old guy seemed to gaze straight off into the distance, not paying him any attention.

"You for real?" Jesse muttered to himself at the end of the day, when his TV watching was over and it was time for bed. He was curled up on the sofa, in his pajamas, his bare feet stuck between the cushions.

His mother brought in a mug of hot chocolate for each of them. She turned off all the lights and they sat together in the glow of the fire. It seemed to make the room quietly shimmer.

"We should do this every night," chirped his mother, sipping her hot chocolate. "We could sit and chat. You could tell me about your day and I could tell you about mine."

"Bor-r-r-ring."

"No way," replied his mother as she looked up at the mantel. "Right, Santa? Not with Christmas coming. No way."

TWENTY-TWO DAYS
TO CHRISTMAS

When Jesse's eyes were closed the Santa did seem real. Or was it a dream? Did he see the light flicker in the fellow's lantern?

The next morning he ran from the bedroom only to find his mom sound asleep on the sofa. She had a book on her stomach with her finger between the pages. She was in the same clothes she had been wearing the night before.

His eyes jumped to the mantel. Santa with the lantern was gone. But in his place was another guy. It looked to be Santa nestled in an armchair. Jesse stepped closer and discovered an open book in his lap.

Jesse looked at his mother and banged his foot against the brass guard in front of the fireplace. Her breathing fluttered. He banged it harder and she woke.

"Gosh," she said, "I don't even remember closing my eyes." She sat up. "I told you he'd be back. The House of Wooden Santas has a fellow who sure loves books — good ol' *Reading Santa*. I'd say this guy hardly turns on a television."

Jesse's head swerved to another part of the room. To where the TV was *supposed* to be. "Again!" he yelled.

"And this time it's not coming back."

"Mom!"

"I've thought it over very carefully and I've decided it's best for both of us. Maybe now you'll see there are other things you could be doing."

"No TV! Not even one program?"

"Not one."

Jesse moaned. "Sick."

"And that means video games, too."

"Really sick."

"It'll be fun. You'll find lots to do."

Jesse sat rigidly on the sofa. He tried to imagine his world without television. What would he do while he was waiting for supper? What would he do on Saturday mornings? What would he do in the middle of a snowstorm?

"Bor-r-r-ring," he told his mother. "Extremely and absolutely bor-r-r-ring."

"Santa doesn't think so."

Jesse turned his eyes to the mantel. The fellow did look happy. But only because his mother had made him that way. And besides, he didn't get dragged away to live in some place where there was never anything to do!

"I bet you can't do it," his mother said.

Jesse knew what his mother was up to and wasn't about to fall into her trap. He sat on the sofa

and hardly moved. He pretended not to hear a thing she was saying. The longer she talked the more he stiffened, until she gave up and went to the kitchen to make pancakes.

At the breakfast table, just as he was pouring on the syrup, his mother said, "This is Sunday. So what do you say we go to church?"

Jesse didn't reply.

"Maybe we'll see someone we know. Maybe you'll see some of your friends from school."

Jesse sneered. "I don't have any."

Church did turn out to be better than Jesse expected. The pews were as hard as those in his old church, but the music was a lot better. There was even a guitar and drums, and sometimes people clapped their hands to the songs.

After the service Jesse's mother tugged him off to social hour in the church basement. He had just bitten into a chocolate cupcake when he realized Mrs. Wentzell was standing next to them.

"Good morning," their landlady said to his mother. She was looking grouchier, Jesse thought, than she did with the yappy dog in her arms.

"Good morning."

"And how's your business doing?"

"It's a bit early yet. But with Christmas and all, I expect it will pick up, Mrs. Wentzell. Any day now."

"I hope so. For your sake, and the boy's."

"I'm sure it will."

"You can't expect to raise a child without a steady income."

Mrs. Wentzell looked at Jesse, whose mouth was full of cupcake. It was so full, in fact, that crumbs were starting to spill down his chin. She handed him a napkin.

"Thank you," Jesse mumbled. That caused a spurt of more crumbs.

"Jobs are not easy to come by these days," his mother said to Mrs. Wentzell.

"I know that well enough. My daughter had to go all the way to Vancouver."

"That's a shame. And you won't get to see your granddaughter this Christmas?"

Mrs. Wentzell just frowned and left. She hadn't even finished her tea, Jesse noticed. She went out the door, past the minister, who had just walked into the room.

The minister joined Jesse and his mother.

She held out her hand. "Michelle Agnew," she said to his mother. She smiled broadly at Jesse. "I'm the leader of this flock."

Jesse gave her a strange look.

"I'm no sheep," he said.

"And nobody can pull the wool over your eyes, right?"

The two women laughed. Jesse forced a smile.

TWENTY-ONE DAYS TO CHRISTMAS

On school days Jesse had been used to his breakfast on his lap and a half-hour of cartoons. Today his mother insisted he join her in the kitchen. He dragged himself to the table.

"Go-o-o-od morning, my treasure. And what would you like on your cereal this fine and sunny morning?"

She held a banana above his bowl, with a small knife ready to slice it into pieces. She was even singing. "Here comes Santa Claus, here comes Santa Claus, right down Santa Claus Lane. . . . "

"Whatever," Jesse mumbled.

Down came the banana slices. "Sugar?"

"Whatever."

"Under the tea cosy."

Not exactly where he would have thought to look, but his mother had done stranger things before. Jesse lifted the tea cosy. His hand jumped back in surprise. Not a sugar bowl, but another Santa.

"Oh, my," said his mother. "And what have we here?"

As if she didn't know, thought Jesse.

"Popping up in the House of Wooden Santas . . . is . . . *Santa the Woodworker*. He drives a fine nail and strokes a steady saw. And to us he comes complete, house and all!"

Not a word from Jesse.

"Think Santa could build us a house of our own?"

"Wish for it on Christmas Eve," Jesse shot back.

He looked at his mother. She was suddenly quiet. He could see a little sadness in her eyes.

"We're okay, Mom."

She winked his way and showed a bit of a smile. "I guess we've managed so far."

She put an arm around him.

"You're right," she said, her voice quiet. "And I was rather greedy. Santa is for the small stuff."

"Mom, you're squeezing me too hard."

She gave him a slobbery kiss.

"Oh, man." He wiped his cheek with the end of his T-shirt and ran off to get dressed for school. He was out the door then, and through the snow to the bus stop.

He wasn't looking forward to school, as boring as the weekend might have been. School meant work and sitting next to Jonathan.

Jonathan was a torment and he bragged a lot. Especially about his father. It drove Jesse crazy.

If anyone in class had a new game, Jonathan was sure to have played it already with his father. If anyone's dad had a new snowmobile, his father had a better one that went twice as fast. And he knew everything about hockey, Jonathan said, because he'd played it all his life. Plus he met Wayne Gretzky once in an airport.

When Jesse walked into the classroom he quietly asked his teacher if he could be moved, but Mr. O'Donnell whispered, "Hang in there. Jonathan is going through a little bit of a rough time." Mr. O'Donnell smiled at Jesse and left it at that. Jesse walked down the aisle.

Jonathan was already in his seat. Jesse checked his chair before sitting down. The last day it had been gum, and the day before that, melted snow.

"You're in big trouble," Jonathan said to him.

"Me?"

"You'll have to go to the office."

"Yeah, right."

"Yep."

"What for?"

"Marking on your desk."

Jesse looked down. In one corner of his desk, the corner closest to Jonathan, were three words, in rough, heavy pencil letters. They stood out like dirty scars.

They said: *DON'T BELIEVE IT*. Jesse quickly covered the words with his hand.

"You did that," he snapped at Jonathan.

"No way."

Jesse spit on his fingers and slipped them under the hand covering the words. He rubbed hard. He peeked under his hand and saw that most of it was smeared away. He wet his fingers again and rubbed away what was left. Just in time, too, for Mr. O'Donnell was standing at the front of the class, his eagle eyes looking directly at them.

As soon as Mr. O'Donnell turned away, Jonathan started bugging Jesse again. "So, you still believe in Santa Claus. My father says — "

"I don't care what your father says!"

"If you're afraid you won't get presents, that's dumb because you still do."

"You're what's dumb," Jesse said.

Mr. O'Donnell appeared at that moment and stood near their seats like a jackrabbit ready to jump. They stopped talking and started their work. Mr. O'Donnell eased back into his regular, swinging walk. Jesse wished more than ever that he could be moved.

When he arrived home from school that day he was feeling extra sour.

"Okay," his mother said, "what's the big deal? Out with it. I'm all ears."

But Jesse just went off to his room and pretended he had homework to do. When his mother came in and sat on the bed he still refused to talk about it.

"Okay. Suit yourself," she said. "Bet Santa understands."

She left the room. He heard her go into her workroom at the back of the house.

Jesse grunted. "Yeah, right."

TWENTY DAYS
TO CHRISTMAS

O n Tuesday morning Jesse could have stayed in bed forever. No way did he want to get up, even though he'd been tossing and turning for hours.

He lay on his back with the bedclothes tight under his chin, trying to figure out why Jonathan was being so mean. And he could not get out of his head the words Jonathan had scrawled on his desk.

Maybe Jonathan was right. Maybe his mother was playing a game with him. Maybe there was no such . . .

Suddenly something caught his eye. He sprang upright in bed. Suspended from the curtain rod, in the middle of his window, was Santa, tucked inside the curve of a golden crescent moon.

Jesse scrambled to his feet so he was eye to eye with the fellow. His mother, yawning and tying her housecoat, shuffled in at that moment. She stood at the foot of the bed. Now all three of them were at eye level, though his mother's eyes were not open all the way.

"In the House of Wooden Santas," she said sleepily, "hangs our *Santa in the Moon.*"

She held Santa to one side and let go, causing him to swing silently back and forth, back and forth, in front of the window. "He rides high in the sky," she said. She stopped for a few seconds because of a wide yawn. "Takes away the troubles of the day and gently rocks us through the night."

"Mighta worked for you," Jesse said and bounced to the floor. "Sure didn't work for me."

It spoiled his mother's daydream smile. "Jesse," she pleaded with a whine in her voice as he went through the door, "wait."

She stood in the hallway, leaning against the wall outside the bathroom door.

He emerged from the bathroom and glared at her. "Is there such a thing as privacy in this house?" He padded over the wooden floor, straight to the living room sofa. She was right behind him.

"Do you mind?" he said, frowning stiffly, his arms clasped around his legs.

"Jesse, what's the matter? You can tell your mother."

He jumped up and ran off back to his room. He hauled on his clothes. He was determined not to cry, even though he came close to it every time he thought about having to go to school.

Santa's swing back and forth in front of the window had almost stopped. When Jesse finished dressing, he fixed his eyes on him. But filling Jesse's head, like a fearsome drift of swirling snow, was Jonathan's silly grin and his mean and teasing words.

When Jesse arrived in school that morning he pretended he had no time to even look at Jonathan.

But before long, small folded scraps of paper landed on his desk. Jesse ignored them.

Then came the whispers. Jesse tried to ignore them, too. But words crept through, muffled words jabbing at him. "Wimpy . . . bet you believe in elves, too." Followed by a chuckle under Jonathan's breath.

Jesse wanted to look him in the face and roar at him to shut his mouth. But all Jesse did was lean his head against his hand to cover his ear.

There was only one bright spot in his life during the whole school day. Mr. O'Donnell decided on the parts for the Christmas concert.

"For the very important role of the first shepherd," he said, "how about you, Jesse?"

Jesse nodded. He was thrilled to be the first one picked.

"The shepherds are the narrators," said Mr. O'Donnell, "and I know I can count on you to speak clearly and look serious."

"Yes, sir."

Mr. O'Donnell's eyes scanned the room. "For the other shepherd . . . "

Hands shot up all around.

"This part is just as important. At times every single person in the audience will be looking at you . . . Jonathan."

"Yes!" shouted Jonathan.

Jesse's heart sank.

"Jesse, I'm counting on you to help Jonathan *stay* serious. We wouldn't want any grinning or giggling."

"No, sir," Jonathan sighed.

Mr. O'Donnell turned his attention to choosing the other parts.

Jonathan looked over at Jesse. A devilish grin spread slowly across his face.

NINETEEN DAYS
TO CHRISTMAS

Jesse moaned. He groaned. He buried his head in his pillow.

And when his mother entered his room, as he knew she would, he sounded especially miserable.

"Poor baby," she sighed. "Let Mommy have a look."

He took that to be a good sign. Whenever he was sick his mother treated him like a four-year-old.

"My stomach."

She touched it and he flinched.

She frowned even more. "Poor tummy." She drew in a great breath. "Appendicitis."

"No!" he proclaimed. He forgot to moan as he was saying it, so he said it again, "No-o-o-o."

"How can you tell, sweetie?"

"I don't have a fever." He took her hand and put it to his forehead. "And it's not a sharp pain in my stomach. It's kinda like that time I ate too much chocolate."

"Do you feel like you want to throw up?"

Jesse hadn't thought of that. "Well, sort of."

He could see his mother was starting to have doubts, so he shut his eyes and let his head rest on the pillow, moaned slightly again, and pretended to be falling asleep.

She kissed him gently on the forehead. "Maybe you just need more rest. A day home from school."

Finally. The words he had been waiting for. But he didn't stir. He just moaned a sleepy "okay."

Only when he heard his mother leave the room and the door creak behind her did his eyes pop open. He breathed a sigh of relief.

Ah, a day without Jonathan pestering him. A day to himself. If only he had TV.

He heard the door creak. His eyes snapped shut.

He felt the edge of the bed sink under the weight of his mother. He felt the touch of her hand against his cheek.

She tucked something partway under the covers and against his chest. It felt hard. Then she placed his hand gently over it.

She whispered, "In the House of Wooden Santas, snuggled away, is *Snoozing Santa*. He wants you to get plenty of rest."

There was a long silence.

Jesse didn't dare move a muscle. But his brain was doing cartwheels. Oh boy, oh boy, he thought, she's really done it this time. She's turning Santa Claus into a teddy bear. She had her son cuddling into a piece of wood, for heaven's sake. He could end up with a splinter in his chest.

As soon as she was out the door, Jesse turned over on his back and examined the poor guy. He was sound asleep, and Jesse couldn't help but imagine his dreams.

Jesse laid the Santa on his bedside table, stared at him, and nestled down as comfortably as he was.

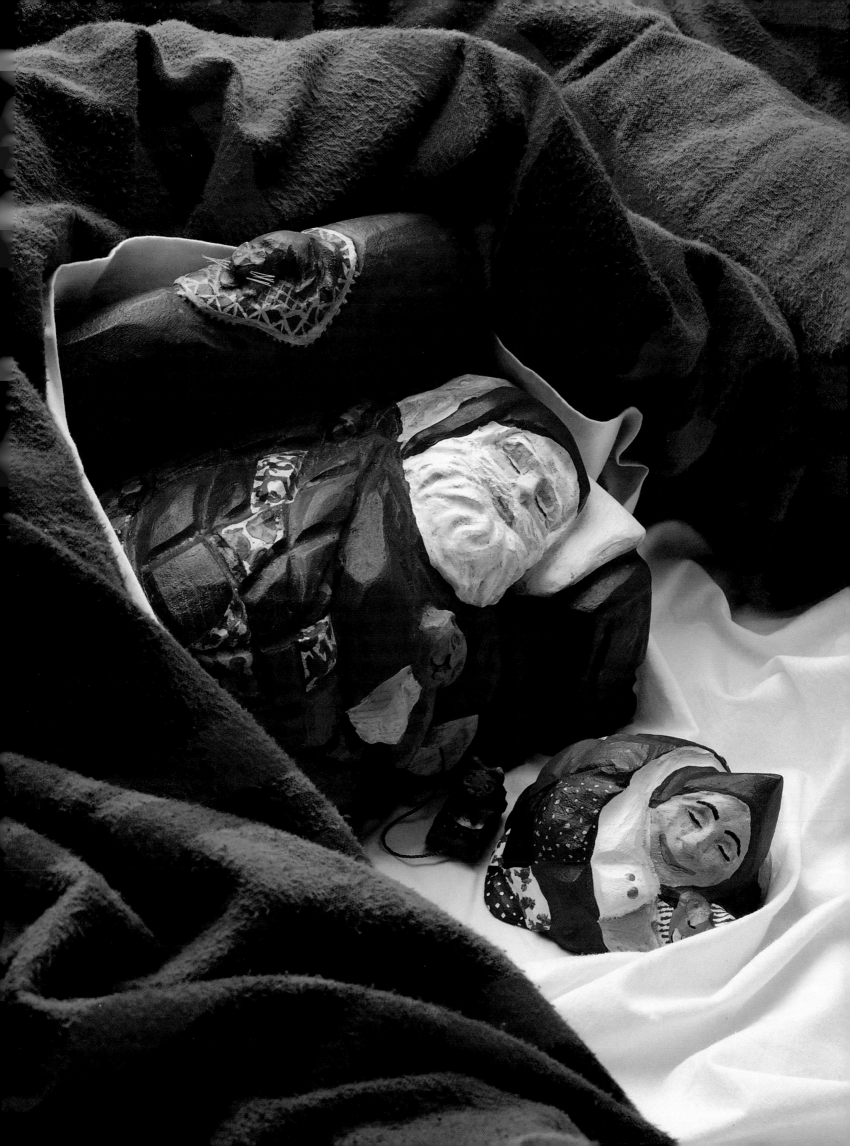

Jesse tried smiling.

He drifted off to sleep.

He was awakened by voices in the kitchen. At first they floated in and out of his head, bits of talk poking at his dreams. The voices seemed to grow louder and give way often to bursts of laughter.

Soon Jesse was wide awake, wondering who besides his mother could be in the kitchen.

He could tell it was a woman. He slipped out of bed and tiptoed to the door. He didn't dare open it wider because it would creak. The best he could do was shut one eye and peer through the crack with the other.

He caught sight of the two of them at the kitchen table, drinking tea. He could see part of the woman's face. It was the minister from the church they had been to on Sunday.

More laughter.

"I better go, I'm afraid." Their voices grew faint as they headed toward the front door. "Thanks for the tea."

"And we'll see you tomorrow afternoon."

"Jonathan's got a net in the basement. The boys can play hockey."

Jonathan? The shock of it caused Jesse to bang his head against the edge of the door. He stumbled back to bed. It couldn't be.

But before long Jesse found out that indeed it was the very same Jonathan.

"Reverend Agnew dropped by and I was mentioning how you were having a little trouble getting used to a new place," his mother said, "and, lo and behold, doesn't she have a boy in your class at school! Now isn't that a lucky coincidence? Just what the doctor ordered."

She was going on and on and hardly stopping for a breath. She took one of Jesse's hands and patted it as she continued full speed ahead.

"I know you're not feeling the best right now, but tomorrow you'll be back to your old self. And after school we'll go over to Jonathan's house, and you two can get to know each other even better than you do now. And won't that be loads of fun?"

"Yeah."

"You don't sound very excited."

"I'm sick, remember." Though he couldn't even manage a moan.

"Ah, poor baby. And here's your mommy keeping you awake."

Jesse's mother pecked his cheek with a kiss, and as she slipped out of the room she whispered, "Just let yourself dream of all the wonderful things your tomorrows will bring."

The door creaked shut.

Jesse moaned.

EIGHTEEN DAYS
TO CHRISTMAS

In the early hours of the morning Jesse heard the wind howl. He could picture a wild storm, gusts of snow so fierce the school would never open.

After one especially loud howl Jesse sprang to the window, only to find there was not a flake of snow in the air. Disgusting. What was the use of stupid wind without any snow?

"Forecast calls for a perfect day," came his mother's voice above the sound of the radio in the kitchen.

"Some chance," Jesse muttered.

He strolled to the kitchen, knowing it was no use to look sick again. His mother would have him out the door and straight to the doctor's office.

"How's your tummy?" she asked.

"Better."

"Knew it." She patted his head. "Terrific."

Breakfast was cinnamon toast burnt around the edges and orange juice that had been mixed with too many cans of water.

"Sorry about that," she said. "I don't know where my mind is this morning."

"Outer space," Jesse said. And his mother didn't even notice.

All during breakfast Jesse expected a new Santa to pop up. His eyes wandered around the kitchen, but there was nothing. After breakfast he took the long way back to his bedroom, through the rest of the house. Nothing there either. He was tempted to peek in the workroom, but then his mother might think he actually looked forward to her Santas.

All the way to school his *own* mind was in outer space.

In his classroom he avoided looking at Jonathan for as long as possible. When he finally did glance his way it was because Jonathan had not uttered a word.

Jonathan's head hung down and his eyes were not budging from the math book in front of him. The book was open to the wrong page.

At recess and lunch hour Jonathan kept to himself and said he had other, more important things to do. When they practiced for the Christmas concert Jonathan knew every one of his lines and didn't laugh once.

Weird, very weird, Jesse said to himself.

When the bell rang at the end of the day, he and Jonathan went their separate ways. And still Jonathan had not said a word to him.

Jesse's mother picked him up and they were off to the grocery store. At the check-out counter she discovered she didn't have enough money with her, and had to put three cans back on the shelves.

Still in outer space, thought Jesse.

At four o'clock they pulled into the driveway of Jonathan's house. As they started up the path Jesse's stomach tightened.

Jonathan's mother met them at the back door. "Come on in. I just this minute put on the kettle."

Jonathan was sitting at the kitchen table, doing his homework and looking just as serious as he had in school.

"You boys can play hockey in the basement," his mother said.

Jonathan disappeared down the stairs as soon as the words were out of her mouth.

Jesse looked at his mother. He could see he was expected to go, too.

He headed to the stairs and almost ran into a man with a walking stick.

"Sorry," Jesse stammered.

"It's okay."

The man wasn't pleased, Jesse could tell, even though there was something like a smile on his face.

"This is Jonathan's dad."

"Oh," Jesse said. He didn't mean to sound surprised. He was thinking, Is this who Jonathan is always bragging about?

He limped past Jesse. He sure didn't look in any shape to drive a snowmobile. Or play hockey.

Partway down the stairs Jesse heard his mother's voice in the kitchen. "Glad to meet you. Michelle tells me you're interested in wood carving."

Jesse stopped to listen.

"I could be, I guess. There's not much to do when you're sick of watching television."

"I'd be happy to give you a few pointers."

"If you want. It's not my idea. But, of course, you know that."

Jesse continued down the steps. Jonathan handed him a hockey stick.

"Fell off a ladder a few months ago and busted his hip," Jonathan muttered. "Had to get a steel pin in it. He's pretty mad with himself for what happened."

"Is it getting better?"

"Not like it should."

The two of them played floor hockey. They took turns being goalie and taking shots on each other. Jonathan didn't brag, even when he scored on Jesse. And not once did he mention about not believing in anything.

His mother brought them fudge cookies and milk, and they sat on the bottom steps and talked hockey. Just like he remembered doing with his friends in the city.

When Jonathan asked him his favorite team in the NHL, he told him the Leafs and Jonathan went, "Yes!" under his breath. Then he said, "My dad said we might fly up and see an NHL game. But I guess maybe we won't now."

"My mom said we might. But I guess maybe we can't afford it."

When it was finally time for Jesse to leave, he asked his mom, "Just five minutes more?"

And as soon as Jesse got home that evening he kicked off his boots and ran to his bedroom to dig out his binder of hockey cards.

He ran right into a new Santa.

A Santa on skates, holding a hockey stick, on top of his bedroom dresser.

"Yes!"

"Into the House of Wooden Santas," his mother declared, "skates *Hockey Santa*. Weaving down the ice, across the red line, over the blue line, past the defense. He shoots . . . "

"He scores!"

"Whatta guy!" she said.

"And he's gonna win 'em the Stanley Cup." Jesse held Santa over his head like a trophy, pretending to skate around the room and shouting, "Yes!"

"Yes," agreed his mother. "Finally. Yes!"

SEVENTEEN DAYS
TO CHRISTMAS

As soon as Jesse arrived in school on Friday morning he raced off to find Jonathan. He couldn't wait to show him his hockey card collection, especially his Leaf rookies.

Jonathan took one look and said, "So. Big deal. I got a lot better cards than that."

Jesse snapped his binder shut and walked away.

But not before Jonathan called out to him, "If you believe hard enough, maybe Santa Claus will bring you *Gretzky's* rookie card." It was followed by a dumb laugh.

That card cost hundreds of dollars and Jonathan knew it. It was a rotten thing to say.

Still, Jesse couldn't keep himself from turning around and yelling, "Maybe I will!"

At his desk Jesse thought back to the day before and their good time together. He couldn't believe it was the same fellow.

"They tell you something's true, and then it all turns out to be a pack of lies," Jonathan said. "My father told me so."

Jesse did his best to ignore him the whole day, even at the practice for the Christmas concert when they were standing shoulder to shoulder.

"Hey, guys, you're not very friendly shepherds," Mr. O'Donnell complained. At the end of the practice he asked about their costumes.

"Our moms are working on them," Jonathan said. "His mom is making him a staff. Maybe my dad is gonna make one for me."

Jesse just nodded.

After school, when he arrived home, his mother called from the kitchen, "I just this minute put a Christmas cake in the oven. Wanna lick the bowl?"

Jesse threw down his backpack and threw himself on the sofa. When his mother came into the living room he grunted and raised his lip in a sneer.

"Now what?" she said.

"Jonathan. I hate him," Jesse blurted out. "The guy bugs me and he's a rotten friend."

"What . . . ?"

"He's a pain. He doesn't care about anyone except himself. He's dumb and I never want to talk to him again!"

"Whoa," said his mother. She sat down next to him.

Jesse wiped his eyes and his nose, both at the same time, with the sleeve of his sweatshirt.

"Jonathan's dad is having a pretty tough time of it," his mother said. "The doctors told him he'd be walking on his own by now."

"So. I don't even have a father," Jesse snapped, "and I don't go around saying rotten stuff to people when they're supposed to be your friend."

"You have a father. . . . "

It was the first time Jesse had mentioned his father in a long time. He lived thousands of miles away, and they hadn't been together since Jesse was a baby. Since then it was only Jesse and his mom, except that his father would phone on his birthday and Christmas. There were times he wished he had a father to do things with — like go to hockey games and stuff — but he had his mother and she loved him so much sometimes that she squeezed him to bits. Like right at this very moment.

His mother finally let him go. "It's different. When you're used to having a father in the same house, I mean," his mother said quietly. "Jonathan's dad has a lot on his mind. He was a carpenter, and now he can't work."

Jesse wasn't satisfied.

"Maybe Jonathan gets upset."

"And gets mean with me. For no reason!"

Jesse was mixed up. He wanted to be mad at someone.

"And there's no Santa Claus!" he yelled.

"He said that?"

Jesse grunted, "Yes."

"And you believe him?"

Jesse didn't know what to believe. He was mad and confused and frustrated.

His mother slipped away to her workroom. She returned with a wooden figure in her hands. This Santa was tall and straight, and he carried a walking staff with a star on the top.

"In the House of Wooden Santas . . . "

"Mom," Jesse whined, "I'm sick of these Santa — "

She put a forefinger to his lips and continued, " . . . there's a lot of trust. Santa knows it's not easy to find, especially when people do mean and rotten things."

"So?" he snapped.

"To believe in Santa, you have to search it out, and when you find it, hold onto it with all your heart."

Grumbling silence.

"Trusty Santa we'll call him," she said. "How about that?"

Jesse folded his arms rigidly.

His mother placed Santa carefully on the mantel. "Now," she said, "I need to finish off your staff for the concert. I'm almost done."

Jesse wouldn't look at her. He wouldn't move a muscle.

Only after she had gone did his stiffness gradually slip away.

He glanced at Santa. Maybe it was the scent of pine branches lingering about the room, or the

smell of Christmas cake wafting in from the kitchen, but his mind seemed to drift away to some place where he and Santa Claus were walking down a road, each with a staff in hand.

The telephone rang. Jesse shook his head and blinked.

He dragged himself to the phone. "Hello."

"Sorry, okay?"

"What?"

"Sorry for being so mean in school, okay?"

It was Jonathan. Jesse couldn't think of what to say.

"You still there?"

"Sorry about your father," Jesse said weakly.

"This morning he was acting weird again. He's okay now."

"You gotta have trust," Jesse murmured. It slipped out. He hardly realized he had said it.

"Guess what?"

"What?"

"My dad made my staff today," Jonathan said, "and it's amazing."

"Yeah?"

"Got a star on top and everything. He said he got the idea from your mother. You gotta come over tomorrow and see it."

When Jesse hung up the phone his mother emerged from her workroom. "One shepherd's staff, especially for you. See what I put on the top of it."

"A star," said Jesse, before he even looked.

"Just like Santa's," his mother said.

"And Jonathan's," Jesse murmured, as he held it for the first time.

SIXTEEN DAYS
TO CHRISTMAS

S aturday morning had been cartoon morning. But this Saturday Jesse found himself sitting on the sofa, shepherd's staff in his hand, looking at Santa and *his* staff on the mantel, and thinking about the Christmas concert.

It gave him the most curious feeling. As if he really was out in a grassy field at night. Among the noise and smell of hundreds of sheep. Under the brightness of a star.

When Jesse and his mother arrived at Jonathan's later that morning, Jonathan came rushing down the stairs to meet him, staff in hand.

He handed it to Jesse. It seemed another way of saying he was sorry.

"Jonathan couldn't get to sleep last night," his mother said. "So I told him to count sheep." She laughed.

In the living room they encountered Mr. Agnew. "Great job," Jesse's mother told him.

"Doesn't take much to carve a star."

"Takes a lot to follow one," Reverend Agnew piped up. "Sorry. Couldn't resist." She laughed again.

"We brought something to show you," said Jesse. "Wait till you see this guy."

His mother uncovered Santa from the box.

"Cool," Jonathan said. "And look at what he's got in his hand. Wicked."

Jonathan's mother was bursting with compliments. Jesse felt proud.

His mom put Santa into Mr. Agnew's hands. "You should give it a try."

He looked at the carving, and ran his fingers over the wood. He handed it back to her. "I don't think so."

"You could do it, Dad."

"Sure you could," Jesse's mother insisted. "It doesn't have to be a Santa. It could be anything. I started off with angels."

"Angels are simple," Jesse declared. "Even *I* could do an angel."

"Men don't do angels," Jonathan announced.

His mother bristled. "What did you say?"

"He could do ministers," Jonathan stammered.

"Or moose," Jesse added. "Christmas moose."

They all laughed, even Jonathan's father, a little.

Reverend Agnew led the boys out of the room. "We'll leave them to figure it out. I think you two should go outdoors and play. It's too nice a day to be inside. The fresh air will do you good."

Mothers are all the same, thought Jesse — excited by fresh air.

"Wanna build a rink in the backyard?" Jonathan asked.

His mother whispered, "His dad used to make one every year."

Jesse was none too keen on the idea, though he had to go. No outdoor rink could ever be as good as a real indoor one.

First they cleared away enough snow to form a rectangle, piling it up the sides, and flattening what was left to make it level. Jonathan called it big enough for a good game of hockey.

"Doubt it," Jesse muttered to himself.

According to Jonathan they had to stamp down what snow was left as hard as they could, then flood it. Flood it very carefully several times. It might be days before they would be able to skate on it.

Yeah, Jesse was thinking, skate on it, sure.

Once they saw his mother and Jonathan's father looking at them through a window. Jonathan smiled up at his dad and worked all the harder.

After the snow had been trampled down, Jonathan and his mother rigged up a hose from the laundry room in the basement.

Spraying the water was the only real fun of it, as far as Jesse could see. Jonathan acted like the expert, but he did give Jesse several turns. When they had finished the first flooding, Jonathan stood back and admired their handiwork.

"It's going to be a wicked rink," Jonathan proclaimed.

"Believe it when I see it," Jesse mumbled to himself.

They trailed inside, red-cheeked and starving, and shed their winter gear. Jonathan's mother took a sizzling dish of macaroni and cheese from the oven. The aroma sent the boys scrambling for chairs at the kitchen table.

Jesse's mother could hardly hold in her delight. Jesse could tell what she was thinking — that he had finally found a friend. That it might be the end of him complaining about having to move.

Before he left for home Jesse noticed Jonathan standing next to his father, eyeing the piece of wood in his lap. His dad still wasn't looking too happy, but he was being nicer to Jonathan, acting a bit more like Jesse imagined a father would.

All the way back home in the car, Jesse thought about his own dad. He wondered what his dad would say to him if they met. He wondered if he would know where to phone him this Christmas.

His mother stopped to put Santa in the mail, and back at their house she went straight to her workroom.

That evening she set a small table in front of the window that looked out into the backyard. It was a still, crisp night and the naked porch light caught snowflakes drifting silently from the sky. The fresh glaze of snow sparkled as if it were diamond dust that had fallen over the ground.

Jesse's mom covered the table with a cloth and laid out two china plates and two crystal wine glasses that once belonged to her grandmother. In the center of the table she placed a lit candle, and next to it the newest Santa.

She called to Jesse in her best imitation of a butler, "Dinner is served."

She escorted him to his seat and pointed out their special guest. "Santa, this is Jesse. Jesse, Santa."

"Very pleased to meet you," he said. "Nice shovel you have there."

His mother shook out a napkin with a great flourish and spread it across Jesse's lap. "Can I interest you in some wine, sir?"

"Yes, please."

"Orange or brown."

"Brown."

She poured root beer into their wine glasses.

Jesse lifted his to his nose and sniffed it. "Wonderful fizz."

She uncovered the food. "And for you, sir — chicken legs. Done just the way you like them."

"Ah, superb."

"With peas, fresh from the can."

"Exquisite."

"Shall we begin?"

"Why not?"

"But first we must toast our special guest."

They raised their glasses.

"To a robust man of the great outdoors," said his mother. "Welcome to the House of Wooden Santas. No matter how much snow, he always loves to shovel. He's our — "

"I got it, I got it," said Jesse. "He's our *Fresh Air Santa.*"

"How did you ever guess?"

FIFTEEN DAYS
TO CHRISTMAS

Jesse sat in the car, making silly faces, trying to pass the time until they reached the church.

The service was as lively as the week before, and Jesse found himself singing along with his mother and clapping his hands. He especially liked it when the drummer did the loud bit on the cymbals.

Partway through the service Jesse spied Jonathan sitting by himself several pews away. Jonathan did his spook face that he sometimes did in school when he was tired of listening to the teacher. Jesse flared his nostrils and puffed out his cheeks and made his goof eyes.

Someone in the pew behind tapped him on the shoulder. Jesse's head swiveled round instantly. His goof eyes looked right into the eyes of Mrs. Wentzell! Her head jumped back and her dangling earrings swung like crazy.

She leaned forward to Jesse's mother and said in a low, grumbling voice, "Your boy is being extremely rude."

Jesse turned to his mother and shrugged.

His mother looked back, confused. At the sight of the scowling landlady her eyes grew wide. She offered a half smile, but it did nothing to change the look on Mrs. Wentzell's face.

Jesse glanced at his mom. She was staring straight ahead. She glanced at Jesse. And rolled her eyes.

They sat stiffly together in the pew and stayed that way until, in the middle of the service, Reverend Agnew told a funny story and they both laughed out loud.

Jonathan's mother was good at telling stories, though Jesse could see that not everyone liked them. He sneaked a look behind. The landlady was looking even more grim.

Reverend Agnew paused for a few seconds. "I know some of you have been used to a more solemn service. In church we can be solemn, and in church we can also be joyful. Let's sing together, number three on your song sheet, 'I've got that joy, joy, joy, joy, down in my heart.'"

Just as the first notes were struck on the guitar, Jesse heard a muttering from Mrs. Wentzell. "Disgraceful. My husband would never have allowed the church to be turned into a dance hall." With that she took her prayer book and walked out of the church.

Later that afternoon Jesse heard about the reason for Mrs. Wentzell's sudden departure.

Jonathan and his mom had come by their house. With the school concert only a couple of days away, the mothers had set to work on the shepherds' costumes.

The boys were out of sight in Jesse's bedroom, playing with Lego. But the door was wide open and Jesse heard every word. It seemed Mrs. Wentzell could get pretty crabby when she set her mind to it.

"She sees things a certain way and she's not about to change. She's even worse since her husband died. She hasn't got much patience."

"I know," said Jesse's mom. "She's been calling me and calling me about the rent."

"Can you make a go of it with your carvings? It can't be easy."

"The craft store tells me it should pick up."

"You're sure?"

"I still have a few savings. We'll see."

Jesse walked into the kitchen. He stared at his mother to see how worried she looked.

"Okay, stand up on the chair," his mother said.

She sounded like her regular self.

"Let's see if we can make a shepherd out of you."

She had taken an old bathrobe and cut it down to fit him and used the leftover material for a headpiece. Jonathan's mom helped her tie rope around his head and his waist. When they had finished they looked very pleased with themselves.

His mother found his staff and put it in his hand.

"Never have I seen a more handsome shepherd."

"Doesn't look too ba-a-a-ad," Reverend Agnew said.

Jonathan emerged from the bedroom, anxious not to miss any of the fun. He stood on a chair next to Jesse. Soon there was a pair of handsome shepherds.

"*Ewe* two look great," Reverend Agnew declared. "Get it — *ewe.*"

She was still chuckling when she and Jonathan went out the door, heading home.

Jesse's mother plopped down on the sofa. She looked exhausted. But before long she was up again and on her way to the workroom.

"Mom, you're working too hard. You need to take a break."

"I won't be much longer."

"Are we okay? Are we getting to be broke?"

His mother came to a sudden stop at her workroom door. She walked back to Jesse, sat down in a chair, and held both his hands.

"This is an experiment. Maybe it'll work out, maybe it won't. I have to admit, it hasn't been great so far. I guess it takes time for people to get to know my work. But I believe I can do it, and that should count for a lot."

She hugged him.

"What's this Santa?" Jesse said to cheer her up.

"So, you're looking forward to them now, are you?"

"Well, you know." He forced a grin. "I gotta be there when you need me."

She took his hand and led him to her workroom.

It was the one part of the house he stayed away from most of the time. He knew his mother didn't like it when he showed up unexpectedly and started poking around.

On a table was a Santa, nearly complete.

"Who is he?" Jesse noticed he didn't look particularly jolly.

"He has a lot on his mind, this guy. *Thinking Santa* maybe. What do you say, Jesse? He sits around the House of Wooden Santas thinking about how lucky he is to have people who care about him."

She turned the Santa and now Jesse could see into his eyes.

"And maybe," she said, "he's thinking how tough it is sometimes to have people who depend on him so much."

"He's thinking too hard if you ask me," Jesse declared. "People can only do the best they can do, Mom. That's what you always say."

"Think so?"

"Know so," he said.

He flared his nostrils and made his goof eyes — and kissed his mother on the cheek.

FOURTEEN DAYS
TO CHRISTMAS

For once Jesse was looking forward to school. His mother bundled his costume into a bag, and with help from his shepherd's staff he trudged his way through the snow to the bus stop. Jonathan met him as soon as he stepped off the bus. "We got to shovel every inch of snow before we can flood the rink again. We'll do it after school."

Jesse headed to the pay phone and dialed home to get his mother's permission. She said she would pick him up at Jonathan's house at five o'clock.

During recess and lunch the boys practiced their shepherd lines, and that afternoon at the dress rehearsal they didn't miss a single one.

Mr. O'Donnell was full of compliments. "And your costumes are great, guys, and your staffs are terrific!" He stuck his thumb in the air. "You make a very convincing pair of shepherds. Wow!"

At the end of the school day the boys were so pleased with themselves they almost floated over the snow to Jonathan's house. They burst through the back door, proclaiming the exact words Mr. O'Donnell had spoken.

They discovered Mr. Agnew in the living room, staring vacantly at the TV.

He looked over at the boys, but didn't say a word. Even when Jonathan repeated all the great things Mr. O'Donnell had said.

"Dad, you gotta see the concert."

His father shook his head. He turned back to the TV.

Jesse's eye caught a half-carved piece of wood cast aside on the coffee table.

Later, outside, the boys had little heart for shoveling.

Jonathan sat on a snowbank and looked miserable. "And I thought things were going to get better."

"Everything takes time," Jesse said. "He needs to give it another try."

"What's the use?"

At five o'clock, after he and Jonathan had made another halfhearted attempt at shoveling, Jesse's mother drove up. As Jesse climbed into the car Jonathan turned and headed inside without even saying good-bye.

On their way home Jesse told his mother the whole story.

"What can we do?" he asked when they were in the house and sitting on the sofa.

"I don't know. Jonathan's dad is a stubborn man. Sure doesn't sound like he's about to change."

His mother was standing by the mantel, next to a new Santa. Jesse hardly paid him any attention. She held him up in her hands. "So," she said, "in the House of Wooden Santas . . ."

But Jesse had a lot more on his mind. "Maybe . . . if we wished for it . . ."

"What?"

"I got it. Maybe, instead of presents for Christmas, what we wished for was Mr. Agnew to smarten up."

Jesse's mother stared at him. "I don't know about that. . . . "

"Sure, you're the one who said all that stuff about trust. You're the one who said you got to search it out and hold onto it."

"But this is a lot to ask."

"Forget it, then," he blurted.

"Now, Jesse."

"You make up all these dumb stories about Santa Claus! And now you say there's nothing he can do!"

"I didn't say that."

"And that proves he's not real!"

"I think he *would* help. . . . "

"Okay, then. Prove it."

There was a long period of silence when Jesse knew his mom was staring at him. He wouldn't look back.

She laid Santa in his lap. Jesse wouldn't look at him *or* his mother.

"In the House of Wooden Santas we gotta learn to get along."

"Not my fault."

"This old fellow doesn't like it when we argue. Especially over him."

Jesse pressed his lips together.

"He could be *Wish Santa.*"

"Yeah, right," Jesse muttered.

"You wish for what you want. And I'll wish for peace between us. Whaddya say?"

Jesse thought about it, but he didn't say anything.

His mother wouldn't take her eyes off him. "What have we got to lose?"

Jesse took Santa in his hands and held him out in front of them.

"Okay, Mr. Santa. I made a wish. Whaddya going to do about it?"

THIRTEEN DAYS
TO CHRISTMAS

I t was the big day, the day of the concert.

His mother would be there, of course, and Jonathan's mom.

At the final rehearsal Jonathan's mind seemed miles away.

"That night," said Jonathan, "we were in the fields, keeping watch over our folks. . . ."

"*Flocks,* Jonathan, *flocks,*" interrupted Mr. O'Donnell. He scowled at him.

"It's okay, sir," Jesse stammered. "He'll be perfect tonight."

"The whole class is counting on you guys."

"We won't let anyone down."

Jesse cornered Jonathan in the hallway after the school bell. "You can't mess up tonight with all those people in the audience, all those mothers and fathers. . . ."

Jesse twisted his mouth, but he couldn't take back what had slipped out.

"I know," Jonathan said.

"You got to concentrate."

"Sure," Jonathan muttered and wandered off.

Jesse could do nothing. Nothing except hope.

At least they would have luck on their side. If he could believe his mother, they would. When Jesse arrived home that afternoon, she popped out of her workroom, holding another Santa.

"Ladies and gentlemen. Tonight, riding through the House of Wooden Santas, I present to you . . . someone every performer needs — *Good Luck Santa!* He carries a horseshoe, a rabbit's paw, a shiny penny. So, go ahead, rub his head for good luck."

Jesse brushed his hand over the curve of wood.

"Ta-da!" exclaimed his mother.

She whisked Santa into a box.

"Show's over, I'm afraid." She crumpled up newspaper and stuffed it around him. "I made a wish that this old fellow will bring us *both* good luck. Maybe our Santas will finally start to sell. Christmas Day is less than two weeks away."

As soon as supper was over they were in the car, off to the concert. All the way there Jesse practiced his lines, making sure he hadn't forgotten any of them. He hoped Jonathan was doing the same.

But when he arrived in school, he found it wasn't lines that Jonathan had forgotten.

He was in his shepherd's costume, standing in front of Mr. O'Donnell. Without a staff in his hand.

"Jonathan, how did you . . . ?"

"I just did, sir."

"But it was part of your costume. And all that work your father did."

"I know, sir. I'm sorry."

Mr. O'Donnell walked away, shaking his head.

Theirs was the last item on the program.

A light shone above a wooden stable in the center of the stage. The boys walked slowly up the aisle from the back of the gym, two shepherds leading the angels, the animals, and the Wise Men. In their midst was Mary and Joseph and the Child. The rest of the class surrounded the stable, singing, "O Little Town of Bethlehem."

Jesse spied his mother and gave her a smile as he walked by. Reverend Agnew was sitting next to her. But there was no sign of Jonathan's dad.

Jesse glanced at Jonathan. No staff. No smile. Not a glimmer of hope his father would show up. Pretty sad-looking for a shepherd.

The procession gathered inside the stable, just as the carol ended. Jesse looked into the audience.

There was Jonathan's dad!

Now Jonathan saw him, too, sure enough, making his way slowly up a side aisle. Jonathan's staff was in his hand.

He encountered Jonathan's teacher and handed him the staff. Mr. O'Donnell made his way to the stable and quickly passed it to Jonathan.

Jonathan broke into a smile. His dad raised a hand to him, and Jonathan gave him a wave with his staff.

It was time to begin the narration. The two shepherds took turns telling the story of the Birth, with the others in the stable each delivering a line when the shepherds mentioned them by name. All except for the Child. To the Child the choir sang "Silent Night" with the whole school joining in on the final verse.

Neither Jonathan nor Jesse had missed a line. Their voices were as strong and clear as Mr. O'Donnell had ever wanted them to be. The audience clapped and clapped. Just as the curtain was closing, Jonathan waved to his dad once again.

In the midst of all the excitement, Jesse was thinking about his own dad, that some day he might show up at a Christmas concert.

Later, when the boys had changed out of their costumes and made their way to where the parents were waiting, Jonathan was all smiles. His dad put his hand on his shoulder.

"You did great."

"You changed your mind," Jonathan said.

"After you and your mother had gone, I saw the staff standing there. When I took hold of it I started to think about when I was your age, when I had a part in a Christmas concert. I guess I really wanted to see you on that stage."

"Thanks a lot, Dad."

"It was worth it. Best pair of shepherds I ever saw."

Jesse's mother insisted they all come to their house. They ended up, the five of them, around the kitchen table, a pot of tea and a pile of toast in the center.

"A fine way to end the day," Jesse's mother declared.

"Are you shepherds available on the twenty-fourth?" Jonathan's mother asked all of a sudden. "I'm sure there must be some way to fit you into our Christmas Eve service at church."

Jonathan and Jesse looked at each other. They didn't have to think about it twice.

"Wicked!" said Jonathan.

"Could you come up with a word that's a bit more . . . suitable?" Reverend Agnew's face was as twisted as if she had bitten into a lemon.

"Awesome?" Jesse said.

"Wild?" Jonathan said.

"I was thinking more along the lines of . . . wondrous."

"Guys," Jonathan's father said, "that's what shepherds are. Wild and woolly and *wondrous!*"

TWELVE DAYS
TO CHRISTMAS

So," said his mother when Jesse appeared at the door of the workroom, "Jonathan's
dad showed up at the concert. Santa came through in the crunch."

"Think my wish really had anything to do with that?"

"Helped, I'd say. Wouldn't you?"

Jesse walked into the room, thinking hard about it.

His mother had let him sleep in because he had been so late getting to bed the night
before. "I called Mr. O'Donnell," she said. "We had a long chat. He's a nice man. I let him know
you wouldn't be in school until this afternoon."

Jesse loved surprises. His mother had another one for him.

"How would you like to do some painting for me?"

She had never suggested such a thing before. Jesse thought he could never be of much help,
although he had sometimes painted ornaments for their Christmas tree.

She took a figure out of the cabinet behind her and placed him on the table. He was bare,
unpainted wood. He looked like he was about to fly.

"This guy could do with some color on his cloak," his mother said. She laid out a clean brush
and a small pot of scarlet paint.

Jesse had never seen such a Santa. He began in earnest to paint the fellow's cloak, while his
mother sketched on paper some things she might put in his hands.

Jesse loved it — he and his mom working together, school far off, Christmas so near.

The doorbell rang.

His mother went to answer it, leaving Jesse hard at work. But his brushstrokes came to a sudden
stop. He heard the bark of a dog. And a voice that put a knot in his stomach.

He set aside the brush and peered down the hall. There, standing beside his mother, was Mrs.
Wentzell — and Ivan in her arms.

The dog yapped at Jesse. The voices fell silent. Jesse's mother walked back to him.

"That's okay, love. You finish what you were doing."

Jesse returned to his painting. His mother closed the door.

Something was up. He put his ear to the door. He couldn't make out what they were saying. He
eased the door open just a crack.

"You can't do this," his mother said, her words quick and anxious. "I should have the money soon."

"I think I've given you more than enough time," said Mrs. Wentzell. "I would like you out of
the house by the first of January."

"It's Christmas."

"I'm sorry."

"And we couldn't possibly find another place around here."

"I'm sure you won't have to go far."

And with that Mrs. Wentzell was gone.

It was minutes before Jesse's mother returned to the workroom. She didn't look at Jesse. But he could see how angry she was.

Jesse kept it in for as long as he could, then broke into tears.

"Hey, no need of that. We'll figure out something," his mother said. She put an arm around him.

"How did she get to be such a crab?!"

"Who knows?"

Jesse dried his eyes. People had no right to be like that! Especially at Christmas.

Jesse went back to his painting. With every stroke of the brush he was more and more determined to figure out something that would make Mrs. Wentzell change her mind.

Jonathan's father had changed his mind. Sure enough.

Maybe he and Santa — and maybe Jonathan, the three of them together — could come up with something that would work on the crab, too.

"You like this place now, I guess," his mother said, trying to be her regular self.

"Maybe."

She caught his eye. There appeared on his face the barest hint of a smile. It met her own sluggish one.

"Maybe Santa Claus will help us."

Her smile widened a bit. "Really?"

"Yeah, why not?" said Jesse, sounding tough about it all.

She picked up Santa Claus and held him in the air with one hand. She had him flying over the table.

"From out of the sky, swooping into the House of Wooden Santas," she said in a voice too dreary. She turned up the volume and tried to add some spark to it. "With fire in his eyes and passion in his heart! Is it a bird? Is it a plane?"

"No," shouted Jesse, "it's *Super Santa!*"

"He's decided to scour the world for crabby people who don't know the meaning of Christmas!"

"But this guy doesn't look much like a super hero," said Jesse. "His cloak is too heavy."

"The woodworker will just have to work her woodworking magic. She can chip away to reveal a *Super Santa* suit. She can shape a few muscles. She can shed a few pounds."

Jesse was feeling a lot better.

"Now watch as I begin by turning his scarlet cloak into a Christmas cape."

Jesse's mom, chisel in hand, started the transformation.

It took several hours, and Jesse had to go off to school before *Super Santa* was complete.

But that night, when his mother flew the fellow into Jesse's room, he was every inch a super hero.

Jesse lay in bed, his hands behind his head, and stared at him and wondered how in the world they could ever transform the heart of Mrs. Wentzell. It might not be easy.

Jesse remembered the look Mrs. Wentzell had given him in church on Sunday.

It might be next to impossible.

ELEVEN DAYS
TO CHRISTMAS

"Nothing's impossible," Jonathan said after school that day.

They were standing on top of a snowbank, looking down on a sheet of water turning into a sheet of ice.

"You thought *this* would be impossible, didn't you?" he said to Jesse.

"Well . . ."

"Well, tomorrow we skate."

"And the next day we fly!" exclaimed Jesse. "Like Santa!"

"I don't think so."

They plopped down on the snowbank. Neither of them said a word for a long time.

"Maybe if we went to her house and . . . " Jonathan couldn't think of anything else.

"Maybe if we phoned her or wrote her a letter," said Jesse.

"What would we say?"

"That she can't do this. We all got rights. That nobody can be *that* mean."

The more Jesse thought about it, the more he figured it would never work. They dragged themselves into Jonathan's house.

"So down in the mouth," said Jonathan's father when they had gotten rid of their winter clothes and had sunk into the living room sofa. Jesse couldn't tell whether he was being funny or serious. There was an odd kind of shyness in the way he was looking at them.

"Got something to show you," he said.

The boys followed him through a back door to the garage. Standing on an old table, surrounded by wood chips, was a carving. The boys looked at it, then at each other.

The carving was bigger and rougher than anything Jesse's mother would have done, and it wasn't painted, but there was no mistaking what it was.

"He's us," Jonathan said.

It was a carving of a shepherd boy carrying a staff. He looked like Jonathan or Jesse on the night of the concert.

"Maybe I'll try another one," his father said. "And have a pair of them. Think I should?"

It was the first time Jesse had ever seen Jonathan's father pleased with himself.

"Cool," Jonathan said.

"Wondrous," Jesse said.

The other two laughed.

"I gotta tell Mom," said Jonathan. "She'll go nuts. And your mother."

Before long he was back, dragging both of them from Reverend Agnew's office.

"Wow!"

"It *is* good. I mean it," said Jesse's mom.

"He never told me a thing," said Reverend Agnew. "I suspected he was up to something, but I wouldn't dare ask what it was."

"He's going to do another one," Jonathan announced proudly.

Jesse's mom clenched a fist. "Terrific."

When Jesse and his mom left for home she was sounding cheerier than she had all day.

"Got to look on the bright side," she said, pulling into their driveway.

As she unlocked the front door, the telephone rang. She kicked off her boots and scurried to get to it, calling back, "Could be worse, you know."

Jesse crashed on the living room sofa. The Christmas decorations seemed to hang limp. What would be the fun of Christmas if right after it they would have to pack up everything and take off and never ever see this place again?

His mother walked into the living room and stood over him. Her arms were folded, and her lips tight together. Her eyes widened.

"It *is* worse," she said.

Jesse sat up and she sat next to him.

"That was the craft shop." She put an arm around his shoulders. "They *thought* they had sold two of the Santas."

Jesse's head fell against his mother.

"A man bought one, then returned it for a refund. His wife didn't like it. Wanted something with real velvet and lace."

"Puke," Jesse said.

"Wasn't fancy enough for her furniture."

"Gross."

"Someone else put one on hold. Never showed up again."

"What a dummy!"

His mother built a fire in the fireplace. They ate pizza in front of it and listened to Christmas music.

"There's no need to worry," she insisted.

Jesse lay on the sofa and slowly sank into a daydream world of other Christmases. His mother covered him with a quilt.

Later that evening, through heavy eyelids, he saw his mother bring in a figure and put him on the mantel. Santa sat with his legs hanging over the edge, his ankles crossed.

Jesse's mother sat on the floor beside the sofa. She whispered, "In the House of Wooden Santas sits *Santa of Times Past.* He's our memory of better days, when we knew for sure what each Christmas would bring."

Jesse heard faint strains of his mother's voice, soft verses of a song, the one about a white Christmas.

Later the doorbell rang. It broke Jesse's sleep. He heard the voice of his teacher.

He did not move. Just opened one eye from time to time.

"Sorry if I startled you," Jesse heard him say.

"You didn't really, Mr. O'Donnell," answered his mother.

"Keith," he said. "I belong to a local service club. We do what we can this time of the year for those families that might use a little help. We're distributing some Christmas hampers. Thought you and Jesse might like one."

"No, thank you."

"It's just people helping each other, quietly doing what we can."

"I would prefer we pay our own way, Mr. O'Donn . . . Keith."

"I understand. It's just that Christmas can be an expensive time for a lot of people. It's just to ease the load a bit."

Jesse heard the crunch of snow. A long time passed without a sound.

Jesse heard the crunch of snow again. He saw Mr. O'Donnell walk down the hallway, a heavy box in his hands. There was a thud on the kitchen floor.

"Would you like a coffee?" his mother said.

"I'd love one."

Jesse could hear their voices in the kitchen. His teacher talked about his work. Jesse's mother talked about hers.

"I'd love to see one of the Santas . . . if you wouldn't mind."

His mother tiptoed into the living room. Jesse shut both eyes. He opened one again as she was leaving. She had Santa in her hand.

"Gee," Mr. O'Donnell said. "And it's all carved by hand?"

"Machines that can do this work are a little hard to come by."

"Sorry."

"That's okay."

"It's wonderful."

"Thank you."

"How much would you charge? I mean, are they expensive?"

She told him the price. There was a long pause in the conversation.

"A lot of work involved, as you can see."

"Of course."

Another pause.

Then Jesse heard the crumple of newspaper.

He saw Mr. O'Donnell pass down the hallway, carrying a shoebox. Saw his mother standing there, waiting for Mr. O'Donnell to leave.

Saw in her hand a clump of money.

TEN DAYS
TO CHRISTMAS

When Jesse woke he was in his bed. But something was weird. Something was missing.

He sat at the kitchen table, blurry-eyed, his hair bent in all directions. One look at his mother and he remembered.

"Where's the guy for yesterday?"

His mother smiled. "Sold. Gone. Out the door. Money in the pocket."

Jesse stared at her. "Really?" he said, trying to sound surprised.

"Called him *Santa of Times Past.* Reminded me of the Christmases we used to have."

"Who bought him?" As if he didn't know already.

"Your teacher. Last night. Must have heard about my carving. He came by . . . when you were asleep . . . asked to see a Santa. Bought him right there on the spot."

Jesse looked away and finished his breakfast.

"The big number one. This is the start. I can feel it in my bones."

Jesse didn't know what he was feeling in his bones.

All during school that day Mr. O'Donnell kept giving him odd looks, as if he knew he wasn't paying attention, just pretending to.

"Jesse," he said, after the bell had gone that afternoon. "So . . . your mother carves Santas."

"Yes, sir."

"Think she might come to class and talk about it? There's only five school days until Christmas holidays, and I was thinking . . . what can we do this year for a special treat?"

"Probably she would, sir."

"Don't think she'd mind," said Jonathan. "She showed my dad. And my dad is very stubborn."

Mr. O'Donnell smiled, as if his whole world had brightened. "Fabulous."

As Jesse and Jonathan were leaving, he called out, "Maybe I'll phone her at home. If that's okay. Or drop by your house later. If that's okay."

"Sure."

"That's what I'll do then. I'll drop by. Just for a few minutes. Okay. Perfect." Mr. O'Donnell's smile was bigger than ever.

As the boys left the school, Jonathan said what was on both their minds. "Mr. O'Donnell can be very weird sometimes."

Jesse spied his bus. "See ya," he said. "Tomorrow. Top secret meeting." Then he added in a heavy whisper. "O.W. — Operation Wentzell."

"Got it."

At home Jesse found his mother in her usual spot in her workroom.

"Mr. O'Donnell said he might come by later."

She put down her paintbrush.

"Really?"

Jesse was sure there was excitement in her voice. He looked at her very intently.

"What for?" she asked.

"Who knows?"

She glared at him. "Jesse . . ."

He wouldn't say a word.

She growled and threatened to pounce on him.

He ran off. His mother scurried out from behind the table and chased after him. He raced to his room and fumbled at the door to lock it, but he wasn't fast enough. His mother forced her way in. She just about nabbed him when he squirmed away and darted off again.

Out through the kitchen and into the living room, around the sofa, and back down the hallway, around and around, laughing and yelling at each other all the time. Once he slipped and fell flat on his rear.

He thought for sure she had caught him. But he wormed through her legs, screaming wildly.

Finally she collapsed on the sofa. "I give up!"

The doorbell rang.

"Oh, no . . ."

She tried desperately to get her breath back and look normal.

"Jesse," she called. "It's him. He'll think we're crazy."

Jesse appeared and sagged to the floor, exhausted. "You answer it."

"You."

"No, you."

There was a loud knock.

Jesse and his mother dragged themselves to the door together.

"Hi, Keith . . . Mr. O'Donnell," his mother said. Out sputtered a laugh.

Jesse gave her a hard look.

"Sorry. We were playing chase. It was very funny."

Mr. O'Donnell seemed rather bewildered.

"He wants you to come to school," Jesse said.

His teacher nodded. "To talk to the class about your work. If you're not too busy, that is."

She looked at Jesse and then Mr. O'Donnell. She shrugged. "Sure, why not."

"Great."

"Anything for a laugh." She started to chuckle, but nobody else cracked a smile. "Sorry. I've been in a silly mood all day."

Mr. O'Donnell set a date for Thursday afternoon and left.

"Good-bye," Jesse's mother called as he reached his car. "So long. See you then. Cheerio."

She closed the door and fell against it, and broke out laughing once again.

"Mom, you're cracked."

"I haven't had such a good laugh in months."

"And now Mr. O'Donnell knows you're cracked."

"Did I embarrass you?"

"Yes."

"Oh, well." She covered her mouth with her hand to hold the laughter in.

When she had wiped her eyes for the final time she wrapped an arm around Jesse and dragged him into her workroom. She grabbed the newest Santa with her free hand.

All three of them fell to the living room sofa in a heap, Santa on top.

"A day should never go by without a chuckle, eh, *Jolly Ol' Santa?* No matter what. That's why I invited you to this crazy House of Wooden Santas, right? To keep us laughing."

She handed him over to Jesse.

"He'll put the merry in your Christmas and the happy in your New Year!" Laughter bubbled inside her, then burst out.

"Cracked," Jesse said.

She placed Santa carefully on an end table. "Ummmm . . ."

She raised her hand and wriggled her fingers over Jesse. Before he could squirm away she got him in the ribs.

All he could do was laugh and laugh and howl and laugh.

NINE DAYS
TO CHRISTMAS

"Jonathan says not to forget your skates," Jesse's mother called out to him. She had just hung up the telephone.

Jesse looked out his bedroom window. The frost overnight had made wonderful patterns on the glass. His eyes traced the crystal swirls.

Sunshine flooded the world outside. The snow gleamed. Jesse could see smoke rising straight up from the houses at the end of the road.

Jesse dug out his skates from the back of the closet. He sat on the corner of the bed for a while, looking them over. He touched the blades with his thumb. They were still sharp. It brought back the memory of his best goal ever, that time he deked the goalie on a breakaway and scored to win that play-off game.

He put the skate guards on the blades, tied the laces together, and slung the skates over his shoulder. It would be good just to have them on his feet again.

The rink wasn't nearly as bad as he had imagined it. The ice was rough in places, and he couldn't build up any speed like he loved to do, but it was crazy fun to take a flying leap into a snowbank and lie there under the sky, the snowflakes drifting around him, and his breath billowing out in clouds.

Of course he loved the fact that he scored tons of goals on Jonathan. When two other boys saw them having so much fun, they showed up with their skates and the four of them made teams. Jesse and Jonathan were the Leafs, and right then and there they played the final game for the Stanley Cup, and of course the Leafs won!

They celebrated the first day on the rink with Mr. Agnew's pea soup and dumplings. Jonathan ate three bowls of it. And Jesse, even though he never liked soup much, finished off a second helping. His mother showed up with a plateful of cookies just as they finished — raspberry jam-jams, still warm.

"When I was a little girl my mother would make these every Christmas," she said.

"Deadly," said Jonathan, and scooped up another one.

Reverend Agnew smiled. "Doesn't Christmas make you long to be a child again? The sounds, the glimpses of secrets that made you so excited you couldn't sleep?"

Jesse's mother said, "I remember getting a letter from Santa Claus. . . . "

Jesse had been sitting through it all without saying a word. But the more they talked, the more excited he became. It was building up a fantastic idea in his head.

He couldn't stand it any longer. He dragged Jonathan away to the basement, pretending he had to show him some new hockey move.

Jonathan grabbed his stick, but Jesse took it out of his hand and led him to a corner of the basement, where there was no chance they could be heard.

"I don't get it," said Jonathan.

"I got this brain wave," said Jesse. "I got a way to make Mrs. Wentzell change her mind."

They slapped each other's hand as if they had just scored a goal.

"How?" said Jonathan.

"We get her in the Christmas spirit, like she must have been when she was a little girl. Then she'll have to change her mind. Remember: 'Peace on earth and goodwill to men.'"

"And women," said Jonathan. "But what if she's been crabby all her life?"

"C'mon. Nobody can be that bad."

Jonathan was thinking. "You're right," he said. "There's nobody who doesn't try to be at least a bit good this time of the year . . . just in case." Then he added, "Okay, where do we start?"

"First thing we do is scout out her house. Then we start making plans."

"You mean Operation Wentzell goes into action?"

"Right."

"Now?"

"Right. Now."

They left the house with a secret mission. They were supposed to be going to the convenience store to spend some of Jonathan's allowance, but what they were really doing was going to the store, spending the money, *and* scouting out the Wentzell house. It was up a side road, not far from the store.

As it came in sight, they took to the woods and approached it under cover of some pine trees. They chewed long shoestrings of red licorice and took careful note of every important detail about the house.

"Chimney," said Jesse.

"That means fireplace."

"No wreath on front door."

"That means doesn't like Christmas visitors."

"No Christmas lights on tree in front yard."

"That means hates Christmas."

The boys were secretly hoping Mrs. Wentzell would come out the front door and pass right by without seeing them, but they had no such luck.

On the way back to Jonathan's house they tried to figure out what they would do with all the information they had gathered so far.

"If . . . " Jesse started, but gave up. He summoned new courage. "If she's going to get the Christmas spirit, then the first thing she's got to do is believe in Santa Claus."

Jonathan didn't say anything.

"Right?"

"I guess so."

Jesse looked him in the eye.

"What if there isn't one?" Jonathan said weakly.

"What if there *is?*" Jesse snapped back. If everyone had to see everything before they could believe in it, then nobody would believe in God, either."

"I know that."

"This could be your test," said Jesse. "If Mrs. Wentzell gets the Christmas spirit and changes her mind, then there is a Santa Claus."

"If she doesn't, there's not?"

"Exactly."

"Wicked," said Jonathan.

The boys paused for a minute, as if they needed time for it all to sink in.

"So how do we get Mrs. Wentzell into the Christmas spirit?" Jonathan asked.

"For that we go to the guy himself."

"Santa Claus?"

"Yep."

Jonathan stared at Jesse. He didn't get it.

"You gotta have trust," said Jesse. "That's what my mother says."

That night Jesse sat on the sofa and studied his mother's newest Santa for the clues he was looking for.

"In the House of Wooden Santas . . . " said his mother.

"Wait."

She looked at him curiously.

"I'm trying to concentrate," said Jesse.

He ignored his mother and stared at the wooden figure. She left the room and went into the kitchen.

"In the House of Wooden Santas . . . " Jesse began.

"Hey," said his mother as she came back in the room, sipping a mug of tea, "that's my line."

"Shhhh . . . " With a finger to his lips Jesse continued, " . . . is a Santa who is trying to tell me something. He's saying . . . "

Jesse closed his eyes and concentrated even harder.

"He's saying . . . I am *Santa of Family and Friends.* She has never forgotten their good times together. In this sack are the memories. Dig them out. See them, hear them, feel them. . . . "

His mother kissed him and exclaimed, "You came up with that all by yourself. You're *so* precious."

Jesse opened his eyes.

He was a bit stunned for the moment. "I had help," he stammered.

He really did. It was as if Santa had put a staff in his hand and pointed him to the sack. In the sack he found what he was looking for.

His mother was smiling broadly.

Jesse didn't have the heart to tell her. But his mother wasn't really the "she" he and Santa were talking about. Nope, the sack had to be opened for someone else.

And tomorrow he and Jonathan would be the ones to open it. And start the digging.

EIGHT DAYS TO CHRISTMAS

As soon as church was over that morning, Jesse made a beeline for Jonathan. The two of them squeezed ahead of everyone else, down the stairs to the basement of the church. They went straight to the chocolate cupcakes, then hurried off to a corner by themselves.

"Mrs. Wentzell wasn't in church this morning," said Jesse.

"She's probably home thinking up new ways to be crabby," grunted Jonathan.

"She won't be for long."

Jesse told him excitedly how he and Santa had come up with the answer he was looking for.

"Really?" Jonathan said, looking more than a little confused. "But what does it all mean?"

"It means," said Jesse, "the first question we got to ask ourselves is: What is the most exciting thing that could ever happen to her at this time of the year?"

Jonathan started to think about it.

"Got it," said Jesse, who had done a lot of his thinking beforehand. "Getting a letter directly from old Santa himself."

"Exactly what I was going to say," Jonathan mumbled through a mouthful of cupcake.

They finished off their cupcakes, feeling very pleased with themselves. Jesse began looking about for his mother.

"She's talking to someone," Jonathan said. "It's Mr. O'Donnell." On their way over to them Jonathan whispered in Jesse's ear, "Never saw him in church before."

"A pair of shepherds, is it?" Mr. O'Donnell said, bright and cheery.

"Hello, sir," the boys answered in unison.

"Mom, I really need to go over to Jonathan's after lunch."

"We'll see."

"Ple-e-ease," said Jesse. "I have to."

"It's okay," said Jonathan. "My dad will be home. He won't mind."

Mr. O'Donnell turned even brighter. "This sounds promising."

Jesse's mom started to say something and stopped. She started again. "Mr. O'Donnell has invited me to go snowshoeing with him this afternoon."

Jesse was stunned. "Really? In the woods?"

He just couldn't picture his teacher and his mother in the woods together. With big clumpy snowshoes on their feet.

"By yourselves?" he said.

"I think we better be going, Jesse." His mother put her arm around him and led him away. "Jonathan, your mom is probably looking for you."

They left Mr. O'Donnell standing there, drinking his coffee alone. "I'll see you later?" he said.

Nobody answered him. Jesse's mom gave him a weak smile.

"Weird," Jonathan whispered in Jesse's ear and took off.

Jesse and his mother were in the car and halfway home before either of them spoke. Finally Jesse couldn't hold it in any longer. "A fellow's mom doesn't go snowshoeing with his teacher. Especially Mr. O'Donnell."

His mother laughed.

But she wasn't agreeing with him.

"Weird," Jesse said.

"He *was* acting rather strange. But he *is* nice."

"For a teacher." Now Jesse was very confused.

He didn't want to talk about it anymore. There was enough craziness in his life already. Why the heck did his mother have to add some more?

When his mother called him to lunch Jesse found a Santa in the center of the table. He ignored him.

He ate without a word.

"The silent treatment," said his mother. "Haven't seen that one for . . . must be at least a week."

Jesse growled under his breath.

During dessert she started to hum, then chant, "In the House of Wooden Santas . . . *Music Santa* stands, not saying a word. Just playing his music."

Jesse pressed his lips together. He was determined not to find it one bit funny.

"Wonder what he's playing? 'Silent Night' maybe. Maybe it's 'O Come, All Ye Speechless.'"

Jesse pressed his lips together even more tightly. But his lips couldn't stand the pressure, and out sputtered a laugh.

"Santa knows," said his mother, "that silence can make beautiful music."

Jesse rolled his eyes.

Oh no, he thought, now she's going to sing. So he jumped up from the table and went for his coat and mitts.

"Okay, let's go!" he shouted.

Finally she drove him to Jonathan's house. As he was getting out of the car, she said, "Maybe I won't go with Mr. O'Donnell."

Jesse turned back. "Go if you want to go, but don't talk about me. And don't get in one of your goofy moods."

With that he was gone. He ran up the path and into the house. He escaped inside without even ringing the doorbell.

"Jonathan!" he called out.

"Come on up!" Jonathan yelled from the top of the stairs.

Jonathan had a pencil and paper and an envelope all set out on his desk. He had also done some investigation in his mother's office and found out Mrs. Wentzell's first name.

It took a while and a pile of crumpled-up balls of their rough copies, but eventually they had their letter. Jesse read it aloud as one final check.

Dear Little Alma:

I hope you have been a good little girl this year. Have you?! I know that sometimes it is hard to be nice to people, but remember that Santa only comes to good girls and not nasty ones. If you haven't been good, there is still time before Christmas Day. If you don't try, there'll be a wondrous big lump of coal for you.

Lots of love, Santa.

Jonathan had drawn a picture of Santa with a speech balloon that read: *Santa's watching you. Ho! Ho! Ho!*

"This should get her in the Christmas spirit," said Jonathan.

"Maybe Santa sounds a bit tough," Jesse said.

So they decided to add a P. S. to the letter. It read: *If you turn out to be a real good girl, Santa will fill your stocking to the very brim.*

And with that they folded the letter and put it in an envelope. Jonathan printed *Little Alma* on the front of it.

When they approached her house later that afternoon, with the envelope safely tucked inside Jesse's coat, they found her driveway empty.

"Great," declared Jonathan.

He kept watch on the road while Jesse ran to the front door.

Jesse slyly drew out the envelope, looking all around as he did. He tried pushing it under the door but there was no space. He tried wedging it between the handle and the door frame, but it kept slipping away.

"Car!" Jonathan shouted, scampering into the trees.

Jesse darted about, trying to find some place to leave it. Finally he dropped it on the doorstep. He quickly made a snowball and plopped it on top of the envelope so it would not blow away.

He raced into the trees. Jonathan pulled him down flat to the snow.

Mrs. Wentzell's car turned into the driveway.

They peered through the trees as she walked from the car to her front door. Her eyes fell on the envelope.

She picked it up and brushed away the bits of snow still clinging to it. She seemed to have trouble reading the words.

Her head straightened up quickly. She looked all around.

Jesse and Jonathan snapped their heads out of sight.

They slowly lifted them up again. Mrs. Wentzell had gone inside, the front door closed behind her.

Jesse could only stare at the door and imagine the joy on her face and the warm glow filling her heart.

"First stage, Operation Wentzell . . . complete," Jonathan announced.

"Santa alert, Santa alert!" Jesse proclaimed.

SEVEN DAYS
TO CHRISTMAS

Outside the House of Wooden Santas . . . " Jesse's mother began, the first thing in the morning, smiling broadly from across the kitchen, " . . . some fellow's heard the call of the wild."

She howled a little, like a young wolf.

Okay, thought Jesse, what's up now? He gave his mother a sharp, eagle eye.

She howled a little more. "This woodsman is wild about nature. He knows every bird and beast by name. He can spot a partridge at a hundred yards. He can snowshoe better than the snowshoe hare."

Yeah, now I get it, Jesse said to himself.

On the kitchen counter was the red wool toque his mother had been wearing the day before. She held it upright by its tassel. "Here he is . . . " and she howled again just as she whipped the toque up from the counter, *"Santa of the Wilds!"*

"Mom," Jesse said with a growling whine.

His mother grinned mischievously.

At school that morning Jesse came face to face with Mr. O'Donnell acting even more strangely than his mother. During the opening announcements Mr. O'Donnell looked as if his mind was in the clouds, floating around the classroom. When it landed on Jesse, it came with a long, bright-eyed smile that reminded Jesse of an overgrown elf.

Each time his teacher looked at him, Jesse couldn't help but think of his mother and Mr. O'Donnell tramping through the woods on snowshoes.

When Jesse arrived back home his mother was hard at work. He poked his head in her room. "Heard anything from Mrs. Wentzell? Do we still have to get out of the house?"

His mother dropped her paintbrush and looked at him with suspicion. "Are you up to something?"

"I was just wondering . . . if she called . . . maybe."

His mother's eyes filled with concern. "No, dear."

Jesse left before she had chance to ask any questions.

He phoned Jonathan right away. "No word. Nothing," he told him.

There was a lot of grumbling and then a long silence.

"Guess we need a stage two," said Jesse finally.

"Guess so. Dad said she's a tough nut."

They chuckled a little.

"Time to bring out the nutcracker," Jonathan said.

They chuckled a little more.

"Wow!" said Jesse.

"What?" said Jonathan.

"Nutcracker. Get it? Santa's magic must still be at work in my head. Wow. . . . "

"What? You mean . . . "

"Sugar plum fairies and all that."

"Operation Wentzell, stage two?"

"Exactly."

They worked out a plan. That night Jesse would call up Mrs. Wentzell, and as soon as she answered he would play music from *The Nutcracker* over the phone. They each looked up Mrs. Wentzell's number in the phone book, and when they agreed they had the right one, Jesse wrote it on his hand.

"I can see her dancing now!"

"A little girl again," Jesse said, "dancing with the spirit of Christmas!"

They could hardly wait.

After supper Jesse went straight to clearing away the table and running the water for his mother to wash the dishes.

"You're being very helpful tonight," she said, suspicion still in her voice.

"I know you're anxious to get back to work." He looked at her as if she were acting strangely for no reason.

Jesse set out his school books on the kitchen table and started his homework. The second his mother went into her workroom he called out, "Okay if I put on some Christmas music?"

"That would be lovely. Turn it up loud enough that I can hear."

From his jeans pocket he plucked a tape with "The Dance of the Sugarplum Fairy" on it. He slipped it into the boom box on the kitchen counter. He had to wait out "The Twelve Days of Christmas," which seemed to go on and on forever. Finally, with the twelve lords a-leaping, Jesse turned up the music a couple of notches, then dialed Mrs. Wentzell's number. All but the last digit.

As soon as the sugarplum fairy took over, he hit the final number on the phone. He held the receiver close to his ear, but not so close it would block out the music.

Someone picked up the phone. A dog was yapping in the background. "Hello." Definitely Mrs. Wentzell.

Jesse held the receiver in the air and as near to the boom box as the cord would stretch. He couldn't help but do a little sugarplum dance, just as he imagined Mrs. Wentzell was doing in her own kitchen that very second.

"Jesse!" The yell of his mother from her workroom.

Jesse stared at the receiver in his outstretched hand! He ran to the phone and banged the receiver back in place.

"Jesse, turn the music down! It's too loud. How can you concentrate on your homework?"

He couldn't, not now.

The telephone rang.

Mrs. Wentzell?! He panicked. "Mom!" he yelled. "Could you get that! I gotta go, bad."

He ran to the bathroom, locked the door, and sat on the toilet cover, in dread of what might come next.

"Jesse, it's for you."

Jesse winced.

"It's Jonathan."

"I'll be right there."

He flushed the toilet, then hurried to the phone.

His mother held out the receiver. "That's quick. You don't look well. You don't have diarrhea, do you?"

"Mom . . . " He took the receiver.

Jonathan was laughing.

"It's not funny," Jesse groaned.

It was several minutes after his mother finally drifted back into her workroom before Jesse could whisper to him about his rotten luck with Mrs. Wentzell.

"Maybe she didn't hear."

"Maybe she's deaf. Yeah, right."

"Maybe she hung up before it happened."

"Either way, it was a disaster."

There was glum silence.

"Guess we'll just have to figure on a stage three," said Jonathan.

More glum silence.

SIX DAYS
TO CHRISTMAS

Stage three took place in the freezing cold outside Mrs. Wentzell's.
Jonathan tried to be funny by calling it stage "tree" because of the fir tree that stood in Mrs. Wentzell's front yard, but he wasn't laughing much.

Jesse was especially serious because he had just spent all his money, the money he had been saving to buy a Christmas present for his mother, on lights for that very tree. With no guarantee it would make any difference to Mrs. Wentzell's Christmas spirit.

"Christmas tree, Christmas tree," Jonathan had said that day in school, when they were trying to figure out what to do next. "She definitely needs a Christmas tree."

The plan was to go to her house, hide out until it got dark, then do a quick decorating job on the fir tree.

"Lights," Jonathan had said. "Definitely lights. After the mess-up with the telephone, we got to do something she'll never forget."

Still, Jesse had stood a long time in the store, in front of the Christmas decorations, fingering the money in his pocket. Even though the set of lights was on sale. Even though Jonathan stood next to him and said, "But if it works, it'll be the best Christmas ever for your mother!"

"*If.* Big *if.*"

He reluctantly pulled the money from his pocket.

And now they found themselves in their old spot, in the trees near Mrs. Wentzell's, peering through the branches at her house, Jonathan with the string of lights in his hands and Jesse with the extension cord in his. They had borrowed the cord from Jonathan's basement.

All her curtains were closed. "Now it's plenty dark," Jonathan whispered. "She'd never recognize us, even if the front door flies open and out she pops on the front step."

They rose up, a pair of Christmas gnomes, inching their way across her front yard. At the tree they stretched out the string of lights.

They looked up at the top branches. Neither of them could ever reach that high.

They looked at each other. There could be no argument about who was the heavier and had the broader back. Jonathan sank to the snow. Jesse put one foot on his back, then gingerly brought the other up from the ground to meet it. With a wobbling stretch, Jesse hooked the end of the string over the very top branch . . . before tumbling back to the ground!

He jumped up and grabbed the string of lights. Around and around the tree he went, until he ran out of lights. The bottom half of the tree was still bare.

"I knew we'd need another set," said Jonathan.

"Yeah, right. Forget it."

Jesse took one end of the extension cord and pushed the plug from the lights into it. He handed Jonathan the other end.

"Go for it," he said, pointing to the electric outlet on the side of the house, next to the front door. "I'll wait for you in the trees."

"Why me?"

But Jesse had already scrambled off.

From the hiding spot he could see Jonathan trying desperately to get the plug in the socket. The lights blinked once, then again, and finally lit up the tree!

The top half of it. Red and green and gold and blue, wonderful beacons of Christmas color.

"Whaddya think?" Jonathan said, out of breath, as he scampered into the hiding spot. "Think this will do it?"

Jonathan had an answer to his question soon enough. Mrs. Wentzell, in a great fur coat and slippers, opened the front door and stood there, stiff as a statue. In shock, maybe?

She let out a great grumble. "What now!"

Jesse and Jonathan stared at each other in disbelief.

"And what do you think the police will have to say about this?" she yelled, as if she knew someone was out there. "Tell me, what?" She stood rigid, like a glowering winter witch, scanning the front yard and surrounding trees. "I dare you to show your face!"

Their faces plunged instantly into the snow. And stayed there. Jesse's cheeks were stinging with the cold. And burning and freezing . . . until he could hardly stand another second of it.

He heard the door close.

He hauled up his head. He clawed the snow off his face and out of his eyes. Just in time to see Jonathan scraping and shaking his own snowman head.

"I'm outta here," Jonathan spit out with a spray of snow. He scurried backward, like a mole in reverse.

"Wait . . ."

"C'mon."

"What about the lights? The extension cord? The cops could trace them."

It stopped Jonathan dead in his tracks.

"*You* got to get the extension cord," he declared. "*I* plugged it in."

Jesse groaned at the thought of it. He gazed across the front yard and spied the outlet and the yellow cord coiling over the snow, like a cowardly snake.

He bit his teeth hard against each other. He drew in a chestful of air between them.

"Go for it!" Jonathan barked under his breath. "I'll get the lights."

Jesse sprang from the snow. He ran as hard as he could across the driveway, across the front yard, his eyes fixed all the time on the electrical outlet and its snake of a cord.

He was almost there when the front door opened. Jesse hit the snow!

Out scampered Ivan the Terrier. The front door closed again.

Jesse did not budge. He lay there as stiff as a lawn ornament. He heard the flutter of Ivan's short legs over the snow toward him. He felt the poke of Ivan's nose against his head.

Jesse opened one eye and looked up, straight into Ivan's underbelly. Ivan's hind leg started to rise! Gross! Jesse flung himself to his feet.

He grabbed the extension cord from the snow and gave it an almighty yank! It snapped free from the outlet. Its recoil whizzed past Ivan's head.

The dog went berserk. It made for Jesse, yapping and yelping like crazy.

Jesse made for the tree. There was Jonathan, the string of lights free from the branches, except for the end of it hooked over the very top.

Jesse did not stop. He grabbed the lights from Jonathan with his other hand and kept on running. The top of the tree bent down behind him. The string of lights pulled tight and tighter — then snapped free!

Off the boys went like mad, through the snow, down the driveway, onto the main road, the extension cord and the string of lights trailing behind them. Ivan the Terrier in pursuit — scurrying as fast as his stumpy legs could carry him, his barking worse than a police siren.

Finally the dog ran out of steam. He stood and yelped as the boys raced away in the distance.

Jesse glanced over his shoulder. Ivan was trotting leisurely back up the driveway. His owner was calling. "Did you do your business? Did you do your business?"

All that evening the echo of Mrs. Wentzell's voice rang in Jesse's ears. That and his mother's angry words for his staying out after dark without anyone knowing where he and Jonathan had gone.

"More of that secret project, I suppose?"

Jesse would not tell exactly what they had been doing. He thought his explanation of buying a surprise present at the convenience store should be enough to satisfy her.

It wasn't. She even put Santa on her side.

She sat him on the kitchen table as Jesse was eating his bedtime snack. "In the House of Wooden Santas . . . " she began, anger still in her voice.

"That's not very nice. You're supposed to be mad at me, not him."

"In the House of Wooden Santas," she repeated. (A little too sweet, Jesse thought, but he figured it was best if he didn't say anything.) "There's a Santa who is not pleased with children who do not tell the *whole* story."

"But Santa knows the whole story," Jesse said. "He's part of it."

"Part of what?"

"That's a secret. See, Santa is not telling either."

"Not telling what?"

"*Secret Santa* doesn't like tricks." Jesse grinned broadly at his mother, then looked at the figure again. "Do you, *Secret Santa?*"

Jesse waited as his mother rolled her eyes.

"See," said Jesse, "he's not saying a word."

71

FIVE DAYS
TO CHRISTMAS

Jesse answered the phone. He was still in his pajamas.

"I know your mother is there and you can't talk about you know who. Right?" It was Jonathan.

"Right," Jesse said sleepily.

"And us doing you know what, right?"

"Right."

"I just had to tell you that I woke up with this super fantastic plan to get you know who to do you know what. You won't believe it. Wait till I see you. Bye. And tell your mother you're asking me over to your place after school."

Jesse's mother gave him an odd look as he hung up the phone.

"It was only Jonathan."

"What are you fellows up to now?"

"Us?"

"Yes," his mother said, staring at him intently.

"Nothing." It was tough to come up with something better when his eyes were barely open. "He's coming over after school, that's all."

Jesse gave her the sweetest look he could muster.

He took off to get dressed for school. He was out the door with a kiss and ten minutes to spare.

Jonathan was waiting for him when he stepped off the bus. He was jumping up and down, trying to keep warm in the midst of the snow swirling across the parking lot.

He led Jesse to a corner of the school, out of the wind.

"Okay, ready for this?" Jonathan said.

"Yeah. C'mon. Hurry up."

"Do you think Mrs. Wentzell hangs a stocking at Christmas?"

"Of course not."

From his backpack he hauled out a large wool sock. "This is the biggest one I could find. It's Dad's. We fill it up with all kinds of stuff and we leave it on Mrs. Wentzell's doorstep." Jonathan stood tall and silent, as if he were waiting for applause.

Jesse screwed up his face. On her doorstep! After what happened? He must be crazy.

"It's clean," Jonathan said. "I smelled it."

"What kind of stuff?" Jesse said, just to make him think he was considering it.

"You know, *stuff.*"

"We haven't got any money left to buy *stuff.* Remember? We spent it on lights. Remember!"

"We'll use what we already got."

At recess Jonathan snatched away Jesse's apple just as he was about to bite into it. "Item number one," he said. Then from the dark reaches of his desk he dug out several snack boxes of raisins, leftovers from recesses long past. "Old people love these," he declared.

By the time they reached Jesse's house that afternoon the foot part of the stocking was nearly filled. Added to the food was an unsharpened pencil that glowed green in the dark; a reindeer ornament made with a clothespin, pipe cleaners, and a tiny red cotton ball; an eraser that smelled like grapes; and a bookmark in the shape of a Christmas monkey, with a gold-colored tassel for a tail. The last item had belonged to a girl in his math group and had cost Jesse three of his best markers.

At Jesse's house they were hit with a smell that instantly turned on another light in Jonathan's brain.

"Gingerbread," Jonathan said. "Good old-fashioned gingerbread. And old-fashioned people love it!"

"Even if they're not so good."

Jesse's mother had one batch of cookies in the oven and had rolled flat a second pile of dough.

She let them do the cutting. They washed their hands and went to work. They made stars and angels and snowmen, and out of sight of Jesse's mother they made a gingerbread woman with a smile that stretched from one of her dangling earrings to the other.

When they sneaked her into the oven to bake, Jesse declared, "This might warm her heart."

"Yes, sir," said Jonathan. "Yes, sir!"

After the gingerbread woman reappeared and was set out to cool, the boys whisked her away to Jesse's bedroom and packed her in a small box with some tissues. Down the sock she went.

"Now," said Jonathan, "what else you got?"

They scanned Jesse's room. Then turned to his junk drawer and treasure boxes.

The first find was an elf key chain. "Perfect," said Jonathan who had become the undisputed expert in what they could include and what they could not. He dug through it all, holding some of it up for a closer look. What he finally decided on was a pack of Old Maid cards, a sign for hanging on a doorknob that read: *Beware — adults enter at your own risk*, and a bunch of stickers from the dentist's office that had elephants on them with big, toothy grins.

And a Christmas tree ornament that was a Santa playing hockey.

"Can't have that," said Jesse.

"C'mon."

"No."

"C'mon."

"My dad sent it to me." He took it out of Jonathan's hand and put it back in the box. It was the first time he had mentioned his father in front of Jonathan.

"Will you see him at Christmas?"

"Doubt it."

Jesse gave Jonathan a look that said he didn't want to talk about it anymore.

By the time Jonathan's mother came by to pick him up, the stocking was two-thirds full. It made a bulge in Jonathan's backpack.

As he was leaving he whispered to Jesse, "I'll get more stuff at home. I'll stuff that sock till it can't hold another thing."

Their mothers were doing some whispering of their own.

" . . . nothing else either of us can do," Jesse's mother said as Reverend Agnew was going out the door.

The boys looked at each other. Jonathan winked.

A lopsided smile was the best Jesse could come up with.

His mother was in an even worse mood. And partway through their meal that evening she muttered, "I've been thinking about it all day. . . . I'm not sending that craft shop the new Santa. In fact, I'm not sending them any more Santas. There's no point in even making — "

"No way. You can't give up!" Jesse couldn't believe it.

His reaction startled his mother so much she dropped her fork.

"You just can't," Jesse declared. "I won't let you."

"But — "

"No buts." Jesse got up from the table. "Where is he?" There was desperation in his voice.

Jesse tramped off to the workroom. He returned with Santa and placed him in the middle of the table.

"See what I mean," his mother said. "Just look at him. I thought if I went kinda wild he might sell."

He sure wasn't like any of the others. But that was no reason to give up. "He's just different, that's all."

"Crazy, you mean."

"C'mon, start," Jesse said. "Come on."

There was the edge of a smile on his mother's face. "In the House of Wooden Santas there's . . . "

"Come on."

"I'm thinking. I'm thinking."

"There's . . . "

"There's a fellow who always keeps you on your toes. There's . . . there's . . . "

"I'm waiting."

"There's someone who's not afraid to jump off the deep end. There's a guy who's always full of surprises."

"That's it. He's our *Surprise Santa.*"

His mother's smile had grown to full size. She shook her head. "Never a dull moment with him around."

"Yep."

"Wonder what other surprises he might have?"

"You never know," said Jesse. "You just never know."

FOUR DAYS
TO CHRISTMAS

Jesse was excited about his mother coming to his classroom that afternoon.

Mr. O'Donnell was even more excited. "What a treat, boys and girls. Imagine creating Santa Clauses all day long!"

When Jesse's mom finally walked through the door the children burst into cheers.

All except Jesse, who was feeling a bit embarrassed by it all.

"Well," his mother said, "you sure have boosted my Christmas spirit."

Jesse liked it better when everyone turned quiet and his mother talked about her work — how she picked the wood and how she came up with the ideas. She laid out all her carving tools, then some brushes and pots of paint. She held up each tool and described how it was used. She passed around pictures of the first angels she ever made.

And finally the moment they had all been waiting for. From a box, under several layers of crumpled newspaper, she removed a Santa.

"From the House of Wooden Santas," his mother said, holding him up for everyone to see, "rides a world-famous traveler. He's pedaled over to see you today as a practice run, for Christmas Eve."

"Where's his reindeer?" a girl called out.

"You know the rules — no animals in school."

The children laughed and cheered again.

"I think we'll call this guy *Schoolhouse Santa*. In your honor. He's a bit of a student, you know. He loves making lists."

She set him down on a desk.

She brought out a square piece of pine wood. "And soon this will be another dear old Santa."

There was a final round of cheers.

"Isn't she magical, boys and girls?" Mr. O'Donnell said. "Isn't she magical?"

She looked at Jesse and gave him a sly wink.

When the bell rang for the end of school the children filed past the teacher's desk, each one of them patting Santa on the head.

Only Jesse and Jonathan were left.

"You did a terrific job," said Jonathan. "Can Jesse come over to my house?"

"He means," said Jesse when he saw that his mother wasn't quite ready for the question, "can I go over because we're working on that project."

"Oh, *that* project," she said.

She looked at them both, waiting for more. The boys shrugged. She looked at Mr. O'Donnell. He winked.

"I guess so," she said to Jesse.

The boys left her and Mr. O'Donnell by themselves. He winked at her, thought Jesse, he actually winked at her.

"The two of them like each other . . . a lot," said Jonathan.

"Not my mom, no way."

"You saw it. And that can only mean one thing."

"It's Christmas," said Jesse firmly, as if that should put an end to it.

At Jonathan's house they went straight to his bedroom and shut the door. From under the bed Jonathan pulled out what he now called the "O.W. Christmas Sock." It was packed so tightly that it bulged grossly out of shape. Jonathan had tied the top of the sock shut with bright red ribbon in a double knot.

There was no time to lose. They put the sock in a plastic bag and headed downstairs.

They ran nearly all the way to Mrs. Wentzell's.

They hung back in the trees again to size up the situation before making a move. Her car was in the driveway.

Jonathan held the bag out to Jesse.

"This one was your idea," said Jesse.

"Yeah, but you're the one she wants to kick out of the house, remember?"

"So."

Jesse looked at the bag. He slowly reached his hand inside and withdrew the O.W. Christmas Sock.

He took a deep breath. He stood up. With the sock clutched firmly in his hand, its red ribbon fluttering, he charged in the direction of the house, a Christmas knight on a mission of great courage.

He made a wide sweep around the car and headed stoutheartedly up the walkway. He cast steely eyes to the right and left.

When he reached the front step he quickly strung the red ribbon through the handle of the door and tied it in a big bow.

"Hurry up," Jonathan hissed in his direction.

Jesse rang the doorbell and ran for the trees.

"See," he said to Jonathan. "Nothing to it. Didn't bother me one bit."

The two of them peered out from between the trees to see Mrs. Wentzell open her door and catch her first sight of the O.W. Christmas Sock. They loved the way she carefully untied the ribbon and held the lumpy load of good cheer in her hands. She looked all around, then retreated inside, just in time to prevent the escape of Ivan the Terrier.

Jesse wondered if she would yell out something, something loud and especially mean. She never did.

"The spirit of Christmas just came ringing," Jesse proclaimed as they strolled back down the road. "And Mrs. Wentzell opened the door to welcome it in!"

"We got to her this time!" Jonathan yelled. "Yes, sir! Old crabby will never be the same."

The boys headed home, feeling for all the world like a pair of Santa Clauses.

THREE DAYS
TO CHRISTMAS

Inside the bathroom "Rudolph the Red-Nosed Reindeer" rang out. Jesse let his Christmas spirit run wild.

"Last day of school before the holidays," he announced when he came into the kitchen.

"Gee, I never would have guessed," his mother said.

"And something amazing is going to happen. I can feel it."

"What's that?"

"Can't say." Jesse grinned. "We'll just have to wait and see, won't we?"

At school he found Jonathan as wild as himself. During the Christmas party that afternoon the two of them went dancing and prancing like goofy reindeer.

A crazy excitement was running through the class. How they all wished for Christmas Day! They told Jesse they wished they could have a Santa-making mother just like his. "Then it would be Christmas every day of the year!"

Mr. O'Donnell joined in. "Yes, what a lucky fellow you are! What a special mom!"

Jesse gave Mr. O'Donnell a goofy reindeer face, as if it were all part of his Christmas craziness.

"Going anywhere for Christmas, sir?" Jesse called to him when school was finally over and he was heading out the door.

"Not this year."

Too bad, Jesse said to himself.

"See you in church, Jesse. If not before."

Jesse forced a smile.

When he arrived home from school that day, his Christmas spirit was still flying high. He burst into the house singing at the top of his lungs.

"Then one foggy Christmas Eve, Santa came to say . . . "

He kept it up while he got rid of his winter clothes — and while he scurried through the house in his sock feet looking for his mother.

He found her in the living room, sitting on the sofa in front of a fire. Behind her stood a bare Christmas tree.

He fell into her arms on one final note of his song. He drew back. She hadn't said a word.

"Mom, what's the matter?"

"I cut a Christmas tree. Do you like it? We'll have to decorate it soon."

"What happened?"

"It's okay. I took out the box of decorations. Why don't you try the lights first to see if they all work before we put them on."

Jesse didn't budge. He stared at his mother. "You got to tell me."

Finally she said, "I've been talking to Mrs. Wentzell."

All that day Jesse had imagined his mother saying those words, but it was never in the way she said them now.

"We're still behind on the rent. And someone else wants to rent the house. We have to be out of here in a week. It's definite."

Jesse was stunned. And suddenly miserable through and through.

"It's not fair!" he burst out.

All that work, for nothing!

All that time believing, when it was a useless thing to ever do!

His mother hugged him long and hard. Harder than she ever had before.

The doorbell rang. Jesse's mother went to answer it.

Through his misery Jesse could hear the voice of Reverend Agnew. "I told Jonathan. He had to come over right away."

They joined the black cloud in the living room. Jesse let loose a loud, sneering grumble. "There's no one more mean and heartless than Mrs. Wentzell!"

"She's a witch if there ever was one!" Jonathan burst out.

The boys sat on the floor in front of the fire, staring at it. The mothers watched them in silence.

Finally Reverend Agnew piped up, "I refuse to let that woman spoil Christmas."

"I agree," Jesse's mom added, but said nothing more.

"Now then," said Reverend Agnew. "How about I mix some eggnog? Someone put on some Christmas music. Someone open up that box of decorations for the tree."

The boys took their dead-slow time.

"Christmas slugs," Jonathan's mother said and poked them in the ribs to get them moving.

After a while it turned dark outside, the lights on the tree grew brighter, and a jazzy version of "Winter Wonderland" filled the room.

"Maybe it's time for a Santa," Jesse's mother said. "I think we're all in pretty desperate need of one."

"Forget it," said Jesse.

Jonathan shook his head. "No way."

"He let us down. We did our part. . . . "

The two mothers looked at each other. "What exactly *did* you do?"

The room fell silent, except for the music.

"It's a pretty big secret, I take it," said Reverend Agnew.

Not a word.

"Maybe Santa is still working on it," said Jesse's mother.

"I'd give him till Christmas Eve, wouldn't you?" added Reverend Agnew.

The boys grunted. They looked at their mothers with stronger doubts than ever.

Jesse's mother turned down the music and left the room. She returned with a Santa in her hands. She set him down near the boys, in front of the fire.

The boys would not look up at him.

"In the House of Wooden Santas we hope everything will turn out for the best."

"We hope and pray for it," said Reverend Agnew. "Saint Nicholas surely knows the power of prayer. He depends on more than his reindeer to get him around the world on Christmas Eve."

Jesse looked at Jonathan and then at the two mothers. "Yeah, right."

"Tell us another one," Jonathan grunted.

His mother jumped in. "He'll keep us in his prayers, especially now, when we need it most."

"*Prayer Santa* he is," said Jesse's mom.

The boys showed no sign they were even listening until Reverend Agnew began to pray for help through the tough times ahead. "Like lost sheep we are, O God. Help us to find the path to a safe and happy home."

Jesse and Jonathan muttered a stiff "Amen."

"Santa heard that, I bet," said Jesse's mom.

"And I'm sure God did," Jonathan's mother declared.

TWO DAYS
TO CHRISTMAS

When Jesse awoke he had the crazy sensation he was still in school, that he wasn't on holidays, that it wasn't the day before Christmas Eve.

He was sure he heard a school voice, a very familiar one.

Only one person he knew sounded like that. But the voice was coming from the kitchen.

His mother was talking to Mr. O'Donnell in the kitchen, in their own house, on a Saturday morning!

Jesse bolted upright in bed. He rubbed his hands into his face and ears. The voice did not go away. In fact it seemed to grow louder and more pleased with itself.

Jesse crept to his door to hear what they were saying. It was nothing important. He sat back on the bed with relief.

"Mr. O'Donnell came by to see how we're doing," Jesse's mother said when Jesse showed up in the kitchen. "I invited him in for coffee. He brought some doughnuts . . . and a few other things. For Christmas."

Presents, thought Jesse. Oh, yeah. He wondered what besides coffee Mr. O'Donnell had on his mind.

"We're doing just fine, aren't we, love?" she said to Jesse.

"You've sold a few Santa Clauses, I bet," Mr. O'Donnell said, full of good cheer.

She hesitated. "One."

"I see." His surprise mixed with his disappointment. "And the shopping days are running ou . . ."

He looked sorry to have said it.

"After Christmas," he was quick to add. "You'll have better luck after Christmas. Angels sell all year long, I'd say."

"We won't be around to find out," Jesse declared.

Over Mr. O'Donnell's face came a severe frown. It seemed Jesse's mother hadn't told him a thing about Mrs. Wentzell.

Jesse blurted out the whole story — the great secret his mother had *not* shared with Mr. O'Donnell, even though the two of them might *never* see each other again.

To top off the whole story, Jesse announced, "And you won't be my teacher anymore, either."

His mother gave Jesse a very hard look.

She was about to say something to him when Mr. O'Donnell let out a sorry cry, "Not true."

"I would have told you. . . . "

"And absolutely nothing is going to change Mrs. Wentzell's mind," Jesse said. "I know that for a fact. She's a Christmas witch."

"She is that," said his mother.

"And," said Mr. O'Donnell, "she's my aunt."

Jesse winced.

So did his mother. "Not true," she said, her voice trailing away.

Mr. O'Donnell nodded. "It's a small place."

That didn't do much to help Jesse or his mother out of their embarrassment.

"She's a tough bird," Mr. O'Donnell said. "Especially since her husband died. That's why she's having so much fuss with the church. Uncle Marvin was a church warden for so long he thought he owned the place. I guess God is straightening him out on that one."

Mr. O'Donnell chuckled and that gave Jesse the courage to speak again. "Isn't there anyone who can make her change her mind?"

"When she sets that mind of hers to something . . . it's more than I can do to pry it loose."

His mother left the room. Jesse was not surprised when she returned with a new figure in her hands.

"Last Chance Santa," said Jesse, with a sneer.

She frowned.

"What do you mean, 'last chance'?" asked Mr. O'Donnell.

"He means last chance for him to be a good boy," his mother said firmly. "Or he might not get anything for Christmas."

Jesse didn't much care. "I mean last chance for Santa to prove he's for real," Jesse said decisively.

"Santa doesn't have to prove anything," Mr. O'Donnell piped up with a force that caused Jesse to promptly sit upright. "I, for one, believe. And I pity those who don't. Because they miss out on all the fun."

He tapped Jesse on the head with his finger.

"It's up to you," he said.

Jesse's mother was having a hard time coming up with the right words. "In the House of Wooden Santas . . . I guess this is the last chance for Jesse to make up his mind."

Jesse slipped out of the kitchen and sat on the sofa in the living room. He needed to be by himself, away from adults who try to sound like they know it all.

He looked around the room. The tree they decorated the night before had filled the house with a fresh evergreen smell. He thought back to the day his mother had put up the first Christmas decorations. He looked to the spot where the television used to be. He had almost forgotten about it.

His eyes turned to the mantel. He remembered the first Santa his mother had put there. And all the others that had appeared each day since. He missed them. He wished they all could be in this room at the same time. Maybe they'd help him make up his mind once and for all if there was a Santa Claus.

When he told his mother his wish she put down her coffee cup and thought about it for a long time before speaking. "Probably I should put the craft shop out of its misery and bring them back." She smiled. "And it would be great to see them all together."

"Except for one," Jesse reminded her.

"I'd love to go with you," said Mr. O'Donnell. "We could go in *my* car. Lots of room for Santas."

Jesse's mother thought it was a great idea. Jesse didn't say anything.

"Know what?" Mr. O'Donnell said to him. "On the way back we could stop by my place. I think I might be able to come up with that Santa you'd be missing."

Jesse shrugged.

"Hey, I paid good money for that guy," Mr. O'Donnell said, smiling. "Maybe I could be persuaded to let you borrow him . . . *if* you both agree to come to my place for Christmas dinner."

Jesse could feel their eyes on him, waiting for his answer.

"Sure, Mr. O'Donnell," he said. "Might as well. Since it looks like we'll never see you again."

ONE DAY
TO CHRISTMAS

It was a wonderful sight, this trail of wooden Santas.

The line started on the mantel, descended down a stairway of boxes to two tables joined together, and came to an end in the spot where the television had been. Their way was lit by tiny lights woven through pine boughs. A lively crew they were, all bound for Christmas Day.

Jesse, still in his pajamas, sat with his mother on the sofa and followed the line from beginning to end, stopping at each one to remember what had happened on the day that particular Santa had appeared.

And the final fellow, which his mother had completed that morning, stood proudly at the end of the line.

Jesse mouthed the words of his mother, "In the House of Wooden Santas . . . " then sat back, as she continued. He was thinking of the long hours of her work lined up before him.

" . . . we have found a good bit of happiness, a few parts sadness, and lots of fun times together. *Santa of the Years Yet to Come* says that whatever comes our way, we got each other, you and me."

"But, Mom."

"But Mom what?"

"What about Mr. O'Donnell?"

"And what about Mr. O'Donnell?"

"Aren't you in love with him?"

"Jesse!" She drew back. "What a question."

But she wasn't answering it. Jesse began to squirm.

"No, I am not," she said after so much silence that Jesse thought it was never going to end.

She could have done better than that!

"Mr. O'Donnell . . . " she started, then stopped.

Jesse waited. What in the world was taking her so long?

"Mr. O'Donnell is a very nice man. But . . . I don't think you have anything to worry about."

"We're fine, just like we are," Jesse said.

"I think so." She added, "Even if we have to move?"

Jesse had been trying to put that part out of his mind. He just wanted to have a regular Christmas and not think about the rotten things to come afterward. He ignored his mother's question.

But he couldn't ignore Jonathan's.

Jonathan had phoned him, desperate to have one last try at getting Mrs. Wentzell to change her mind. "It's our only chance. Tomorrow is Christmas Day."

"And what would we do this time?" Jesse asked with a groan. "Cook a turkey and drop it on her doorstep?"

Jonathan was dead serious. "I think we should march straight up to her door and say what a rotten thing it is she's doing. And if she doesn't change her mind, we'll tell her off."

"Really?" said Jesse, who couldn't quite believe the eagerness in Jonathan's voice.

"I'm not chicken."

"Just crazy," said Jesse. "She'll call the police on us. She won't just stand there. She'll flatten us."

"And then we sue her! Then she'll have to change her mind."

Jonathan's idea was running wild. But still he wouldn't take no for an answer.

"What have we got to lose?" said Jonathan.

Not much, Jesse had to admit. The time for Mrs. Wentzell to change her mind had all but run out. It was now or never. And Jonathan certainly didn't sound like he was willing to stand by and let *never* come without a final fight.

So that afternoon Jesse found himself walking with Jonathan up the road to Mrs. Wentzell's, the one they had walked so many times before, and every time for nothing.

Jesse tried to stay cool and forget the butterflies that were swarming around his insides. Jonathan was trying even harder. He sang some mad, mixed-up version of "The Twelve Days of Christmas" and fired snowballs at nothing in particular.

They came to the trees where they had hidden themselves before and walked right past them. They came to Mrs. Wentzell's car parked in the driveway and walked right past it.

They stepped on the carefully shoveled path that led right to Mrs. Wentzell's front door, and Jesse said, "I'm not so sure about this," and hoped he didn't sound like a coward.

"Too late now," Jonathan shot back. He continued his march, not missing a step. He pulled off his mitt and stuck his finger on the doorbell just as Jesse caught up with him.

The door swung open immediately.

There stood Mrs. Wentzell, Ivan the Terrier in her arms. The dog started to yelp.

"I saw you coming," Mrs. Wentzell announced.

Jonathan looked her in the eye. And fell dead silent. He couldn't get a word out.

Ivan yelped and yelped, as if he were the one to do all the talking.

Mrs. Wentzell finally shut his mouth with her hand. "Well?" she said to the boys.

"Mrs. Wentzell," stammered Jesse, "Jonathan has something to tell you."

She looked at Jonathan, but Jonathan's tongue was in knots and he was making less sense than the dog.

"Mrs. Wentzell," Jesse began again, "Won't you change your mind? We *can't* go."

"That nephew of mine put you up to this, didn't he?"

Jesse realized the nephew she was talking about was Mr. O'Donnell.

"When he told me he was in church last Sunday I nearly choked. Just because he likes your mother, that's no reason he should be telling me what to do."

Ivan the Terrier's mouth broke free from her hand and he let out a vicious bark, as if to emphasize her point.

Jesse suddenly felt his mother's fighting streak stirring deep inside him. It rose from his stomach, up his swelling chest, and spewed out his mouth in a torrent of fiery words.

"Not fair! You're being a Christmas witch! You don't care about anything or anybody, only yourself. You got a letter from Santa and Christmas music and your tree all lit up. . . . "

"And my dad's stocking full of stuff!" Jonathan stammered.

Mrs. Wentzell's eyebrows stiffened severely.

The cat had been let out of the bag. Ivan yelped louder than ever.

"So," droned Mrs. Wentzell, "I suspected as much."

It was clearly a standoff.

Mrs. Wentzell let her mutt bark all he wanted, as if she were threatening to let him loose to chew off their legs. The boys stood their ground in steaming silence.

Finally Mrs. Wentzell retreated. She stepped backward and took hold of the door handle.

"Don't you know the meaning of Christmas, Mrs. Wentzell?" exclaimed Jesse in one last burst of frustration.

She looked at both the boys, their ruddy expressions stiff and sour, but she did not answer. She closed the door in their faces.

The boys stood there for a second. Then they, too, retreated, winding their way back up the road.

The rest of the afternoon Jesse spent thinking about what they had done. It didn't put him in any mood for Christmas.

That evening he sat on the sofa, his shepherd's staff across his lap, waiting for his mother to finish dressing so they could leave for the Christmas Eve service at church. He looked along the row of Santas.

How could he believe when they never came through for him? He and Jonathan had done all they could. Santa was no more than a wooden statue who sat all Christmas on a shelf, pretending to be real.

He heard his mother heading for the door. His lip curled into a sneer. "Fake," he muttered as he left the room. He didn't bother to look back.

They were met at the church door by Reverend Agnew and a flurry of guitar and piano music coming from the front of the church. The place was filling up, with more people arriving all the time. Reverend Agnew hugged his mom and directed Jesse to the room at the back of the church.

There he found Jonathan dressed in his shepherd outfit, staff in hand. Jesse dressed in a hurry, and the two stood together, two sorrowful shepherds, hardly saying a word to each other.

"Cheer up," Reverend Agnew told them. "You look like two lost sheep." Neither of them smiled.

Later, when they stood before the congregation, one on either side of the stable, they still looked a pitiful pair.

Jesse's mother caught his eye. She kept pointing to her mouth and flashing a smile.

No way, Jesse said to himself.

Then he caught sight of Mrs. Wentzell! There, behind his mother. She had come in through the back door and was slowly walking up the aisle to take a seat.

"Look," Jesse muttered under his breath to Jonathan.

Their stares were interrupted by Reverend Agnew. "Tonight," she said in a voice that filled the church, "we celebrate the coming of the Child. A child for all the world — innocent and loving, playful and caring, forever hopeful."

With each word the boys straightened up a little more.

"This Child is the child in all of us," Reverend Agnew said over the squawks of several babies in the congregation.

She nodded to the boys. They opened the doors to the stable.

They revealed an infant lying in a manger. And around the infant a semicircle of other figures. Two of them were shepherds.

"Dad's shepherds?" whispered Jonathan.

"Yeah," said Jesse.

The boys looked out into the rows of faces and saw Jonathan's dad. He was smiling their way.

All the people sang "Away in a Manger," every word strong and clear.

The boys walked back down the aisle on the last verse, past Jonathan's dad, who had a wink for them, and Jesse's mom, who was wiping her eyes, and Mr. O'Donnell, who was grinning proudly, and Mrs. Wentzell, who was trying to sing but couldn't seem to get all the words out, especially when the boys blurted, "Merry Christmas," to her as they went by.

Later, when the church service was over, the boys gathered with Jonathan's parents for a closer look at the nativity scene.

"We look cool in there," said Jesse.

"And you wanted Dad to make a Christmas moose," Jonathan reminded him.

Mr. Agnew chuckled.

"A marvelous pair," Jesse's mother said, joining them, Mr. O'Donnell right behind her.

They all stood together in the glow of the light shining down on the manger.

Only Jesse saw Mrs. Wentzell approach. Only he had seen her come back in the church after everyone else had gone.

"Could I have a look?" she asked quietly.

The others turned and discovered her standing there. It was a surprise they could not hide. They moved aside to make room for her.

"Of course," said Reverend Agnew.

She drew closer and stared at the figures for a long time.

"My husband always loved the nativity scene," she said. "Christmas was always his favorite time of the year." She picked up one of the shepherds. "Christmas is not the same when it's just yourself."

She replaced the shepherd and started to leave.

She turned back, hesitantly. "I didn't want to come to church this evening, but I had to. It's Christmas Eve. Marvin would never have forgiven me."

She looked at the boys. "I hardly knew what to do. I guess I was like the sheep looking for a shepherd."

She reached out and touched Jesse's staff.

"And when you two opened the stable doors it was like I was seeing inside for the first time. A child again."

For several moments everyone was quiet. There was something else on her mind and she was having a hard time getting it out. "This church needs all you young people," she said finally.

"And old people, too," Jesse said.

"Yeah," said Jonathan. "Right, Mom?"

Reverend Agnew reached out and squeezed her hand.

Mrs. Wentzell said, "I'll be going now. I need to phone my daughter."

She smiled awkwardly and walked away, heading to the back door again.

"Mrs. Wentzell," Jesse's mother called. "I would like you to come and visit us. Tonight?" She looked at the others. "All of you come. It's Christmas Eve."

Mrs. Wentzell hesitated. She looked at Jesse and Jonathan. "Two shepherds and a Christmas witch?"

It sent both of them stammering. Then Jesse said, "But now you got the Christmas spirit."

"And a letter and sock to prove it," said Mrs. Wentzell.

There was a trickle of uncomfortable laughter. The parents looked at each other, perplexed, but joined in.

They carried it along to Jesse's house that night. When Mrs. Wentzell arrived she encountered the winding trail of Santas.

"And tonight of course," said Jesse's mother, handing her a cup of tea, "the fellow himself shows up. The real one."

"He'll be amazed," said Mrs. Wentzell.

She leaned forward for a longer, admiring look at each Santa.

"Mr. O'Donnell owns one," said Jesse, and pointed him out.

His mother whispered something in Jesse's ear.

Jesse thought hard for a moment, then removed *Hockey Santa* from the lineup. "Jonathan owns another." He handed the Santa to him. "It's from Mom and me. Thanks for the rink."

"Wicked," said Jonathan, clutching the fellow.

"I have an idea," said Mrs. Wentzell, being very serious, but with excitement in her voice they had not heard before.

They all listened intently.

"May I choose a couple as payment for the rent you missed?"

"Really?" said Jesse's mom. It caught her completely by surprise.

"My granddaughter would love one. And my daughter."

"It would have to be more. . . ."

"And a few more for the weeks coming up. And maybe some time after that. There are other people I could be giving presents to this Christmas. They'd be thrilled."

"Thrilled enough to come and buy another one?" asked Mr. O'Donnell with a certain mischievous note in his voice.

"Who knows?" said Mrs. Wentzell. "Though your side of the family is pretty tight."

She took great pleasure in seeing Mr. O'Donnell stumble about for words.

"Once the charm of Santa Claus takes hold," she said, "you never know what can happen."

Mrs. Wentzell departed that night with a box packed with enough Santas to keep Jesse and his mother in the house for a couple of months.

Mr. O'Donnell left with his Santa and with a promise to Jesse and his mom that for their Christmas dinner the next day there would be a plump turkey and flaming pudding *and* chestnuts roasting over his open fire.

Jonathan and his parents were the last to go.

"Now I have competition," said Jesse's mom to Mr. Agnew.

"Not for long. Just until the day I can walk with a hammer in one hand and a saw in the other."

Reverend Agnew thanked Jesse's mother again for giving him the idea to start carving. "I don't know what he would have done."

"Driven us nuts," said Jonathan.

His dad made a playful swipe at his rear end with his walking stick. "Is that so?"

"Yep."

He chased Jonathan out the door.

Reverend Agnew was not long after them. "For heaven's sake, be careful! If one of you falls and ends up in a cast, so help me, I'll send the both of you out to pasture!"

Jesse and his mom stood laughing in the doorway.

"Merry Christmas!"

"Merry Christmas!" the others called back from inside their car as they drove away.

It was getting late. And time for Jesse to be heading to bed.

Jesse hung his stocking by the fireplace and sat with his mom on the sofa for a last few minutes, his feet wedged between the cushions, hot chocolate in his hand. The trail of Santas had several gaps now, and perhaps, before Christmas was over, there would be many more.

"You got to believe," said Jesse, between slurps of hot chocolate.

His mother looked at him, but didn't say a word. She put her arm around his shoulder.

"If you didn't believe in something because you couldn't see it, then your life would be very boring," he said. "Right?"

He looked into his mother's eyes until she nodded.

"A carving shows us the good stuff, like friends and stuff, and love, right?" This time he couldn't wait for her to answer. "And if we didn't believe in that, we'd never have it."

She squeezed him so hard there seemed to be Santas dancing before his eyes.

And off he went toward his room, full of love and full of excitement about what Christmas Day would bring.

Before he reached there the telephone rang.

His mother started toward it, but then she said, "You answer it, okay?"

It was his father.

"Guess what?" Jesse said. "So far this has been my best Christmas ever."

There was a long pause.

"You gotta believe it," he said. "We're doing great."

Jesse listened to his father telling him there was a present in the mail for him and he was sorry it was going to be a little late getting there.

"That's okay," said Jesse, "Santa Claus will be on time." He told his dad he loved him and then he said good-bye.

His mother put her arms around Jesse, and after a second try, managed to pick him up. She dropped him into bed.

"Good-night, love."

"Thanks for all your hard work, Mom." He gave her a kiss. "But, Mom, I don't have a Christmas present for you."

"You're my Christmas present," she said, and gave him a slobbery kiss.

He smiled and wiped his cheek.

He curled under the covers and shut his eyes tightly, and immediately, without a murmur, started to count sheep.